D1256249

The Geological Society of America, Inc.
Memoir 95

HETEROMORPH AMMONOIDS FROM THE ALBIAN AND CENOMANIAN OF TEXAS AND ADJACENT AREAS

By

DAVID L. CLARK

University of Wisconsin, Madison, Wisconsin

1965

Copyright 1965, The Geological Society of America, Inc.
Library of Congress Catalog Card Number 65–24054

PUBLISHED BY
THE GEOLOGICAL SOCIETY OF AMERICA, INC.
231 East 46th Street
New York, New York 10017

Made in the United States of America

550/
GP9
no. 95

QE
21
.646m
no.
95

The Memoir Series
of
The Geological Society of America, Inc.
is made possible
through the bequest of
Richard Alexander Fullerton Penrose, Jr.

ACKNOWLEDGMENTS

The writer is indebted to numerous individuals, institutions, and organizations for the progress of this study. The project was made possible by two grants from the Systematic Biology Section, National Science Foundation, while Dr. David D. Keck was Program Director. The initial grant (G–6364) was made while the writer was at Southern Methodist University, Dallas, Texas; the second (G–9808), while at Brigham Young University, Provo, Utah. A supplemental grant from the National Science Foundation was used in covering plate costs of this publication. A Faculty Research Fellowship from Brigham Young University during the spring of 1962 gave time for the completion of the study.

Mr. C. W. Wright has been particularly helpful during phases of this work. His many good ideas stimulated the writer to begin this study. Drs. Arthur Richards, J. E. Brooks, and J. K. Rigby and Mr. J. P. Conlin have been helpful in arranging for the completion of the study.

The following individuals arranged for the loan of many valuable specimens: Drs. Peter U. Rodda and the late John T. Lonsdale, Bureau of Economic Geology, Austin; Dr. Keith Young, University of Texas, Austin; Ed Heuer, Texas Christian University, Ft. Worth; Mr. J. P. Conlin, Ft. Worth; Dr. and Mrs. Zoltan de Cserna, Instituto de Geológia, Mexico City; Dr. Erle G. Kauffman, U.S. National Museum, Washington, D.C.; Dr. J. Schweitzer, Geologisch-palaeontologisches Institut und Museum, Bonn.

Study of the type and comparative material for this project was accomplished at the following institutions: U.S. Geological Survey, Federal Center, Denver, with the help of Dr. W. A. Cobban; British Museum (Natural History), Drs. Errol White and M. K. Howarth; Geological Survey Museum, London, Dr. Raymond Casey; École Nationale Supérieure des Mines, Paris, Dr. M. Fischer; Muséum National d'Histoire Naturelle, Paris, Dr. J. Sornay; Muséum d'Histoire Naturelle de Grenoble, Mr. Breistroffer; collection of General M. Collignon, Grenoble; Museum des Faculties Science de Grenoble, Dr. Léon Moret; Geologisches-Staatsinstitut, Hamburg, Drs. W. Häntzschel and U. Lehman; Friedrich Wilhelm-Universität, Bonn, Dr. H. K. Erben.

Dr. Raymond Casey took the writer into the type English Cretaceous and Dr. Don Reaser aided in west Texas field work.

During the years of this study the writer has been assisted by graduate students including Charles Hightower, Pete Henely, and Tom P. Keel, Southern Methodist University; and Max Pitcher, Gerald Robinson, Phil Cook, and Jaren Swensen, Brigham Young University. Mr. Swensen worked with the writer during several years of this study and his thesis (Swensen, 1963) was concerned with the Anisoceratidae and Hamitidae. The portion concerning these two groups in this study has been freely adapted from his work.

CONTENTS

CONTENTS

FIGURES

TABLE

ABSTRACT

Very little systematic work on the Texas Cretaceous heteromorphs was accomplished during the time that much of the taxonomy of this group was resolved in Europe. In 1928 there were only 20 known genera of heteromorphs from the entire Texas Cretaceous. This study includes descriptions of 53 species of 19 genera which occur in the Albian, Cenomanian, and lowermost Turonian of Texas and adjacent areas. Stratigraphic distribution includes one species from the Goodland-Comanche Peak, one from the Kiamichi, 15 from the Duck Creek, five from the Fort Worth, three from the Denton, four from the Weno, nine from the Pawpaw, six from the Mainstreet, eight from the Grayson and Del Rio, seven from the Buda and Boquillas, one from the Woodbine, and 12 from the lower and lower-middle Eagle Ford.

Correlation and classification with the English Gault and younger ammonoid zones indicates that the Goodland-Comanche Peak is upper-Middle Albian and that the following younger stratigraphic units can be identified with the Upper Albian, Cenomanian, and Lower Turonian European terminology, as well.

The abundant Turrilitidae fauna of the Texas rocks provides excellent examples of paedomorphosis, acceleration, and caenogensis in the evolutionary history.

The Texas Albian through Early Turonian heteromorphs include one species of *Hamites* s. s.; three of *Stomohamites;* one of *Lechites;* one of *Sciponoceras;* six of *Anisoceras;* three of *Idiohamites;* five of *Allocrioceras;* three of *Ostlingoceras,* of which one is new; three of *Pseudhelicoceras,* two of which are new; five of *Mariella;* four of *Plesioturrilites,* one of which is new; one of *Wintonia;* three of *Hypoturrilites,* of which two are new; three of *Turrilites* s. s.; one of *Euturrilites;* four of *Scaphites;* four of *Worthoceras;* one of *Otoscaphites;* and one species of a new genus, *Prophlycticrioceras.*

1

INTRODUCTION AND PREVIOUS WORK

In 1842, d'Orbigny assembled in a single volume the descriptions of almost all known Cretaceous heteromorphs. Lamarck, Parkinson, Sowerby, and Astier, among others, had described heteromorph species prior to d'Orbigny's classic volume. More than 80 species of what was then recognized as less than a dozen genera of heteromorphs from the entire Cretaceous were described. About 50 per cent of these were assigned to either *Hamites* or *Turrilities*. Most of the genera described by d'Orbigny have been divided into numerous taxa during the past 100 years and many of the species he described are still the more common heteromorphs collected throughout the world. Only a few types can be located at the Muséum d'Histoire Naturelle, Paris.

There were numerous occasional references to the Cretaceous heteromorphs in the latter part of the 19th Century (*e.g.*, de Grossouvre, 1894) but the taxonomy and nomenclature changed little until the publications of Hyatt (1894; 1900), Pervinquière (1907), Nowak (1911; 1916), and particularly Spath (1923–1943). Spath concentrated on the classification of Cretaceous ammonoids beginning in the early 1920's. His long list of publications was highlighted by the publication of the 16-part *Ammonoidea of the Gault* (1923–1943) which stands today as the basic reference for Albian ammonoid studies. Spath is responsible for naming about 30 per cent of all post-Aptian heteromorph genera.

The early students of Cretaceous fossils in Texas and most of North America concerned themselves only perfunctorily with the abnormally coiled ammonoids. Roemer (1852), Marcou (1858), Conrad (1855; 1857), Meek (1876), and Shumard (1854; 1860) first described heteromorph species from North America, and later geologists including Hill (1889a; 1889b), White (1880; 1887), and Cragin (1893; 1900) were particularly concerned with the Texas Cretaceous faunas although not with the heteromorphs.

About 20 years after this early work Adkins and Winton (1920), Böse (1928), and Scott (1924) published comprehensive studies of the Texas cephalopods and, although the work of these geologists was not completely provincial, it did not take sufficient consideration of progress which had been made elsewhere, particularly in Europe concerning Cretaceous heteromorphs. In spite of the important contributions to the heteromorph literature in these years, the work concerning the Texas faunas during the 1920's seems to reflect the ideas of the early naturalists (d'Orbigny, 1840–1842; Astier, 1850) to a greater extent than it does that of the later European paleontologists.

Following a brief interval of vigorous taxonomic activity which concerned the Texas Cretaceous faunas during the 1920's and early 1930's (Adkins, 1928; Böse, 1928; Scott, 1928), there was a general unproductive period which

3

was punctuated only occasionally by the works of Stephenson (1941; 1952) and Moreman (1927; 1942). It was during this time that the European students organized heteromorph taxonomy. The publications of Collignon (1932), Breistroffer (1947; 1953), Dubourdieu (1953), Wright (1953), and Spath (1923–1943) appeared, and the *Treatise on Invertebrate Paleontology* (R. C. Moore, Editor, 1957) synthesized the Cretaceous heteromorph nomenclature and taxonomy to a degree not previously obtained.[1] During the 1950's it was possible to find monographs concerning heteromorphs of the European Cretaceous, but practically none of the Texas material had been included, and it was difficult to assign a valid generic and, in many cases, specific name, to Texas Albian and Cenomanian heteromorphs if the assignment were based on North American literature alone. The monographs of Stephenson (1941; 1952) concerning the Late Cretaceous faunas of Texas and the baculitid and scaphitid studies of the Western Interior by Reeside (1927) and Cobban (1951; 1958a) afforded the only aid available to students of Texas heteromorphs. Anderson (1958) included some description of equivalent age material on the Pacific coast. Recently, Young (1958) has reported previously unknown heteromorphs in Texas. His study is the first in almost 20 years to contribute anything new to the understanding of Cretaceous heteromorphs in Texas.

The present study was initiated in order to synthesize the taxonomy of the Texas Cretaceous heteromorphs with the work done in Europe. The object has been a modern classification of the abnormally coiled Albian and Cenomanian ammonoids in Texas and adjacent areas. The time boundaries chosen include the initiation and completion of many of the heteromorph lineages. In conjunction with this study, younger heteromorphs have been studied (Clark, 1963). With the work of Stephenson (1941) considered, there is now a fairly complete coverage of Texas Cretaceous heteromorphs.

---

[1] After this manuscript was submitted for publication, Jost Wiedmann (Palaeontographica, Bd. 118, Abt. A, 1962) described a large heteromorph fauna from the Upper Albian and Cenomanian of Northern Spain. Some of the same genera and species described by Wiedmann are present in the Texas section.

PRESENT WORK

All the important collections of Texas heteromorphs available have been studied for this project, most important of which are those of the Bureau of Economic Geology of the University of Texas in Austin. The years 1957–1959 were spent collecting from the type areas in the northern and central Texas areas. The summer of 1959 was spent in the Trans-Pecos and west Texas area. Most type areas were visited and, in addition, the many new localities exposed in recent road-cuts, *etc.* were visited (Fig. 1). Altogether,

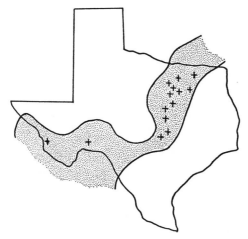

Figure 1. *Locality map showing principal areas of occurrence of heteromorphs in Texas Cretaceous outcrop belt*

more than 5000 specimens of Texas Albian through Turonian heteromorphs have been assembled for this study. All specimens are deposited in the institutions indicated under systematic paleontology.

In 1928, Adkins listed 20 genera and 70 species of Lower and Upper Cretaceous heteromorphs. Arkell and others (1957) have indicated that there are 30 genera of Texas Cretaceous heteromorphs. The present study includes descriptions of 53 species of 19 genera of Albian, Cenomanian, and a few Turonian heteromorphs. Stephenson (1941) described 27 species of eight genera of Upper Cretaceous (Navarro) heteromorphs. This includes two species of *"Turrilites"* and one of *"Hamites"* which belong with other genera. The scaphitids and baculitids of the Austin and Taylor (Upper Cretaceous) plus a few other genera have not been recently studied.

Of the various families of heteromorphs whose age span is such that they could be present in the Texas Cretaceous rocks (Albian-Maestrictian), only the Labeceratidae and Ptychoceratidae have not been reported. *Ptychoceras* has been reported in Mexico (Böse, 1923). The Phlycticrioceratidae have recently been described (Clark, 1963), and the Nostoceratidae and Diplomoceratidae are those described by Stephenson (1941).

The descriptions of the heteromorphs of the Albian-Cenomanian interval of the Cretaceous have been included in a single study because of the close relationships which exist between the various families. The Turrilitidae, Baculitidae, Anisoceratidae, Hamitidae, and Scaphitidae are well represented in the Texas rocks, and all these except the Hamitidae had their origin as distinct families during the early part of this time. Only two of the groups (Baculitidae and Scaphitidae) have many representatives in rocks younger than Cenomanian in Texas.

STRATIGRAPHY

General statement. Perkins (1961) has presented the most recent synthesis of the Albian-Early Cenomanian stratigraphy in the north Texas area. The terminology discussed by Perkins (1961) is applicable in part in central Texas, whereas the west Texas Cretaceous rocks are recognized by a different nomenclature. Because the majority of the Texas heteromorphs described here were collected from the central and north Texas rocks, only the nomenclature which is applicable in that area is discussed. Correlation with other area nomenclature is made.

Winton and Adkins (1920) called most of the stratigraphic units referred to "formations." More recently, Perkins (1961) has considered a number of these same units to be "members." They are described here in ascending stratigraphic order.

Goodland-Comanche Peak Formation. This is the oldest formation in the Texas Cretaceous from which a heteromorph is known.[2] In North Texas the formation consists of alternating limestones and marls, 80–120 feet thick. Perkins (1961) has discussed the terminology problem (Goodland) and other stratigraphic details. A single specimen of one species from this formation is definitely known, although several specimens labeled *Idiohamites fremonti* in the collections of the Bureau of Economic Geology may be from this interval. The one definite specimen is *Hamites intermedius* (= *H. adkinsi* Scott) and is of special interest as it is the only *Hamites* s. s. presently known from Texas.

Kiamichi Formation. This formation has long been recognized as the lowest formation of the Washita Division (Hill, 1901; Perkins, 1961). It consists of marls, clays, sands, and arenaceous limestone up to 40 feet thick. Only poorly preserved molds of heteromorphs have been available for this study, and with the exception of *Idiohamites fremonti* none can be identified.

Duck Creek Formation. The Duck Creek has been interpreted as unconformably overlying the Kiamichi (Adkins, 1933, p. 360), but Perkins (1961) reported no evidence of this unconformity in north Texas. The formation consists of limestones and interbedded marly shales which aggregate 50–60 feet in most areas. The division of this formation into four members, suggested by Winton and Adkins (1920, p. 39–49), does not seem realistic, and Perkins (1961) does not use the smaller divisions in north Texas. This fossiliferous formation has yielded the following heteromorph species:

Anisoceras armatum (J. Sowerby)
A. salei Clark

---

[2] Perkins (personal communication) has obtained a single unidentified heteromorph fragment from an older stratigraphic level in Texas.

7

A. subarcuatum Spath
A. sp. aff. *A. plicatile* (J. Sowerby)
Hamites intermedius J. Sowerby
Idiohamites fremonti (Marcou)
I. varians (Scott)
I. sp.
Prophlycticrioceras tanimum (Adkins and Winton)
Mariella sp.
Scaphites worthensis Adkins and Winton
Stomohamites nokonis (Adkins and Winton)
S. venetzianus (Pictet)
S. virgulatus (Brongniart)
Worthoceras platydorsum (Scott).

The Duck Creek has long been known to contain abundant *Idiohamites fremonti* near the base.

Fort Worth Limestone. This easily recognizable formation is conformable with and normally forms resistant protruding ledges over the softer beds of the underlying Duck Creek. It consists of a series of regularly bedded limestones, with only few marls and shales. It is 25–30 feet thick in the north Texas area.

Heteromorphs collected from this formation include:

Mariella (Mariella) nobilis (Jukes-Browne)
Pseudhelicoceras robertianum (d'Orbigny)
P. serocostatum n. sp.
P. sp.
Stomohamites virgulatus (Brongniart).

Denton Formation. This formation was recognized by Winton and Adkins (1920), but earlier students (*e.g.,* Hill, 1901) as well as Perkins (1961, p. 30) included the Denton as the lowest member of the Denison Formation.

The Denton has been described in considerable detail, including elements of paleogeography and paleoecology by Laughbaum (1960). Extensive faunal lists and measured sections are presented by Laughbaum which indicate that the Denton is 25–30 feet thick in north Texas and consists of extremely fossiliferous marly limestone and shale. It is conformable with the Ft. Worth Limestone below. Laughbaum (1960) lists more than 80 species from this formation, but only three species of heteromorphs in the material studied for this report were labeled Denton. Neither Laughbaum (1960), Perkins (1961), nor the writer collected heteromorph specimens from the Denton. It is possible that the species here listed are from younger stratigraphic units.

Mariella (Mariella) worthensis (Adkins and Winton)
Mariella (Mariella) nobilis (Jukes-Browne)
Stomohamites sp.

Weno Limestone. The second member of the Denison Formation of Perkins (1961) consists of a series of limestones and marls which may attain a thickness of 50 feet. The entire formation weathers to a slope readily. It is apparently conformable on the underlying Denton. Heteromorphs from the Weno include:

Anisoceras perarmatum (Pictet and Campiche)
A. bendirei (Adkins)
Stomohamites venetzianus (Pictet)
Mariella (Plesioturrilites) brazoensis (Roemer).

Pawpaw Shale. The middle "member" of the five-member Denison Formation (Perkins, 1961) is a brownish shale 15–30 feet thick with a few calcareous sands and several shell beds in north Texas. It rests conformably on the Weno and throughout the area of its outcrop it is poorly exposed because of its easily weathered lithology.

This important horizon of the Texas Cretaceous contains the following heteromorphs:

Anisoceras armatum (J. Sowerby)
Hypoturrilites primitivus n. sp.
? *Idiohamites varians* (Scott)
Lechites comanchensis (Adkins)
Mariella (Mariella) worthensis (Adkins and Winton)
Pseudhelicoceras breistrofferi n. sp.
Scaphites hilli Adkins and Winton
Stomohamites venetzianus (Pictet)
Worthoceras worthense (Adkins).

Equivalent rocks in northern Mexico have yielded *Mariella (Mariella) camachoensis* (Böse) and *M. (M.) carrancoi* (Böse).

Mainstreet Limestone. The fourth member of the Denison Formation of Perkins (1961) rests with apparent conformity on the Pawpaw, although there is some evidence of channeling along the base of the formation in Tarrant County. The Mainstreet consists of 20–30 feet of alternating light-gray limestone and marly clay. The following heteromorphs are known from this formation:

Anisoceras perarmatum (Pictet and Campiche)
Mariella (Plesioturrilites) brazoensis (Roemer)
M. (P.) rhacioformis n. sp.
Ostlingoceras (Ostlingoceras) conlini n. sp.
Scaphites hilli Adkins and Winton
S. worthensis Adkins and Winton.

Grayson Marl. This distinctive formation of shale and marl in north Texas forms the uppermost "member" of the Denison Formation as recently defined by Perkins (1961). It is 60–80 feet thick and is conformable on the Mainstreet. The outcrops of this fossiliferous formation have long been favorite collecting grounds of amateurs and students in the north Texas area. Heteromorphs from this unit include:

Mariella (Plesioturrilites) brazoensis (Roemer)
M. (P.) rhacioformis n. sp.
M. (P.) bosquensis (Adkins)
M. (Wintonia) graysonensis (Adkins).

The equivalent Del Rio Formation of west Texas consists of shale and limestone very similar to the Grayson and has about the same thickness. Faunas are largely the same as those in the Grayson but additional heteromorphs present include:

Mariella (Plesioturrilites) brazoensis pecosensis n. subspecies
Scaphites bosquensis Böse
S. subevolutus Böse
Sciponoceras baculoides (Mantell).

Perkins (1961) and Kellum (1956) have reported *Mariella (Plesioturrilites) brazoensis* from the equivalent Aurora Limestone in northern Mexico. The Espy Formation of extreme west Texas also contains *M. (P.) brazoensis pecosensis* n. subspecies.

Buda Limestone.   This thin limestone (1–3 feet) is only locally present in north Texas and in many places has been removed by pre-Woodbine erosion (Perkins, 1961, p. 41). Heteromorphs which occur in this unit are:

Hypoturrilites tuberculatus (Bosc)
Mariella (Mariella) wysogorskii (Lasswitz)
M. (Plesioturrilites) brazoensis (Roemer)
Turrilites (Turrilites) acutus Passy.

The Boquillas Formation of the Trans-Pecos area, equivalent in part to the Buda and the overlying Woodbine, contains:

Hypoturrilites youngi n. sp.
Ostlingoceras (Ostlingoceras) brandi Young
O. (O.) davisense Young.

Woodbine Formation.   An excellent symposium concerning many aspects of the Woodbine Formation has been published (Lozo, 1951). The formation consists of sandstone and calcareous sandstone and was deposited after a time of widespread channeling during the Cenomanian. Therefore, it rests on either Buda or Grayson, depending upon the extent of the predepositional erosion. No heteromorphs were collected from this unit by the writer, and only one species is known in the various collections which have been available for study. This species, *Turrilites (Turrilites) dearingi,* was described by Stephenson (1952, p. 197).

Eagle Ford Group.   This group consists of three units. In ascending order these are: Tarrant, Britton, and Arcadia Park. Heteromorphs have been found in the Tarrant limestones and in the overlying Britton blue shale and thin limestones. The Tarrant is evidently Cenomanian, and the Britton contains the Cenomanian-Turonian boundary. Recently, Swensen (1963) has described heteromorph species common to the Britton and to the lower part of the Utah Tropic Shale. From the Tarrant the following heteromorphs are known:

Turrilites (Turrilites) costatus Lamarck
T. (T.) acutus Passy
T. (Euturrilites) scheuchzerianus (Bosc).

The following have been collected from the Britton:

Allocrioceras annulatum (Shumard)
A. dentonense Moreman
A. larvatum (Conrad)
A. pariense (White)
A. ? rotundatum (Conrad)
Anisoceras sp.
Otoscaphites minutus (Moreman)
Worthoceras gibbosum Moreman
W. vermiculum (Shumard).

There are additional species of heteromorphs from the Britton and younger parts of the Eagle Ford. All listed here are considered Turonian and described in this report because they represent terminal members of families whose origins extend into the Albian.

CORRELATION AND CLASSIFICATION

General statement. One of the best early attempts at correlation and classification of the Texas "Washita" and younger formations was the work of Adkins (1920). This writer pointed out that on the basis of comparison of the total ammonoid fauna known to him the Pawpaw was closer to the Vraconian than to the Cenomanian (1920, p. 42, 66–67). However, he thought that the Duck Creek fauna was typically Vraconian also and, because he evidently considered the Denton to be Cenomanian, he concluded that the Pawpaw should also be classified ". . . provisionally as Cenomanian . . ." (p. 44).

Böse (1928), working with the advantage of Spath's earlier report (1923) on British biostratigraphy, correlated the Fort Worth with the *aequatorialis* subzone of the middle-Upper Albian Gault. He also correlated the Denton with the *substuderi* zone and the Weno and Pawpaw with the youngest or *dispar* zone of the Upper Albian Gault. Böse also considered the Mainstreet-Buda sequence as Cenomanian and preferred to withhold judgment on the Vraconian terminology problem (1928, p. 168).

Spath (1942) revised his earlier Albian zonation and recognized six subzones in the Upper Albian (Fig. 2). These zones, from oldest to youngest, are: *orbignyi, varicosum, auritus, aequatorialis, substuderi,* and *dispar-perinflatum.* The *orbignyi* zone was considered the lowest of the Upper Albian overlying the uppermost Middle Albian *cristatum* zone. The highest Albian subzone, *dispar-perinflatum,* is overlain by the Cenomanian. Except for occasional references in the systematic portion of his monograph, Spath made no attempt to correlate the Texas formations with the Gault.

Breistroffer (1947) argued for the usage of Vraconian, at least in France. He pointed out that the Vraconian in France was different from the Upper Albian because many groups of ammonoids present in the Upper Albian were absent in the Vraconian and many groups appeared in the Vraconian for the first time. He also considered the *cristatum* zone (uppermost-Middle Albian of Spath) to be basal subzone of the Upper Albian in France (Fig. 2).

Spath (1942) Wright &Wright (1951)		TEXAS STRATIGRAPHIC UNITS	Breistroffer (1947)
Lower Turonian	*labiatus*		Cenomanien
	plenus	EAGLE FORD	
Cenomanian	*subglobosus*	WOODBINE	
	varians	BUDA	
		GRAYSON—DEL RIO	
		MAINSTREET	
Upper Albian	*dispar- perinflatum*	PAWPAW	Vraconien (Pleurohoplitien)
	substuderi	WENO	
	aequatorialis	DENTON	
	auritus	FT. WORTH	Upper Albien (Hystérocératien)
	varicosum	DUCK CREEK	
	orbignyi	KIAMICHI	
Middle Albian	*cristatum*	COMANCHE PEAK	

Figure 2. *Correlation and classification of Texas Cretaceous stratigraphic units with European stages and zones*

Breistroffer further referred the entire *cristatum-auritus* zones to the Upper Albian (Hystérocératien) and the overlying zones (Spath's *aequatorialis, substuderi,* and *dispar-perinflatum*) to the Vraconian. On the basis of the entire ammonite fauna, Breistroffer also classified the Duck Creek-Fort Worth formations as Upper Albian (Hystérocératien), the Weno-Pawpaw as Vraconian, and the Mainstreet-Del Rio as Lower Cenomanian.

In the Texas Cretaceous there is no marked break in the heteromorph faunas of the Duck Creek-Fort Worth and the higher beds. Many families and genera of heteromorphs are present in the Albian rocks and in the younger Cenomanian and Turonian rocks as well. Because of this, the usage of Vraconian does not seem to be justified or utilitarian in Texas; and the Upper Albian zonation, as proposed by Spath (1942), and the Cenomanian and Lower Turonian zones, as recently summarized by Wright and Wright (1951) for western Europe, are here adopted for the Texas stratigraphic units.

The classification indicated in this report is based primarily on species of heteromorph ammonoids. Correlation of other Cretaceous stratigraphic units throughout the world with these zones has been determined in some detail by Spath (1942) and Breistroffer (1947).

There are sufficient conspecific heteromorphs in the Texas and British rocks which afford some precision in intercontinental correlation and classification. In addition, there are many Texas species very similar to European species and which probably represent similar evolutionary stages. These have been used with those forms conspecific to effect the classification indicated in Figure 2, and the evidence for this is summarized further on.

Middle Albian. The oldest known heteromorph in the Texas Cretaceous is from the Comanche Peak-Goodland sequence. This species was described as *Hamites adkinsi* by Scott (1928), but it is here considered as a junior synonym of *Hamites intermedius* J. Sowerby. It occurs at the top of the Lower Gault (*cristatum* subzone) and at the base of the Upper Gault (*orbignyi* and *varicosum* subzones) in England. The *cristatum* subzone is considered to mark the upper part of the Middle Albian and, because of the age relationship with the rocks above in Texas, the Comanche Peak-Goodland sequence is considered to be late-Medial Albian. Ranges of species are shown in Table 1.

Upper Albian. In the English Gault, the first *Idiohamites* species appear in the *orbignyi* subzone. The Kiamichi-Duck Creek sequence contains the first *Idiohamites* in Texas, and the Kiamichi, which contains *I. fremonti,* most likely belongs with the *orbignyi* subzone which is lowermost Upper Albian (earliest-Late Albian).

The Duck Creek contains *Anisoceras armatum, A. salei, A. subarcuatum, Stomohamites venetzianus, S. virgulatus,* and *Scaphites worthensis* which are of some regional value. *A. armatum* occurs in the *auritus* to *dispar* subzones of the Upper Albian, and *A. salei* is quite similar to the large *Anisoceras* (*e.g., A. saussureanum*) which are present in the *auritus-aequatorialis* subzones of the Gault. *A. subarcuatum* is known from the *varicosum* to *auritus* subzones, and *Stomohamites venetzianus* and *S. virgulatus* occur first in the *aequatorialis* subzone. *Scaphites worthensis* is as primitive as *S. circularis,* the oldest *Scaphites* in Europe which occurs first in the *varicosum* subzone. Also, *Hamites intermedius* is present in the Duck Creek and that species occurs as high as the *orbignyi* and *varicosum* subzones of the Gault. All these considerations indicate that the Duck Creek contains elements which occur from the *orbignyi* through the *dispar* interval of the English Upper Albian, but the comparisons would indicate that the Duck Creek is most likely *varicosum* and *auritus.*

The Forth Worth contains *Mariella (Mariella) nobilis,* known from the *aequatorialis* through *substuderi* subzones of the Gault, *Pseudhelicoceras robertianum,* known from the *orbignyi-auritus* interval, and *Stomohamites virgulatus,* known first in the *aequatorialis* subzone. These considerations plus the relationship of the older and younger heteromorph faunas in Texas suggest an *auritus-aequatorialis* age for the Fort Worth.

The Denton contains *Mariella (Mariella) nobilis* and other nondiagnostic heteromorphs. *M. (M.) nobilis* occurs in *aequatorialis-substuderi* subzones and is here considered to belong to parts of both intervals.

The Weno contains *Anisoceras perarmatum,* known from the *aequatorialis-dispar* subzones, and *Stomohamites venetzianus,* which occurs in the *aequatorialis-substuderi* interval. An *aequatorialis?, substuderi-dispar* age seems reasonable for the Weno.

The Pawpaw contains a large heteromorph fauna but lacks many forms conspecific with the Gault. *Anisoceras armatum,* known through the *dispar* subzone of the Gault, and *Stomohamites venetzianus,* known through the *substuderi* subzone, indicate a very Late Albian age for this Texas formation. Species of *Lechites* and *Scaphites* in the Pawpaw are similar to the *varicosum-dispar* species of the Gault. One very important species in the Texas Pawpaw is *Hypoturrilites primitivus* n. sp. *Hypoturrilites* has not been previously reported from below the Cenomanian. This species has many characteristics indicative of a very primitive form of the common Cenomanian Turrilitidae and it may be the ancestral form. Also, the equivalent "Vraconian" rocks of Mexico (Böse, 1923) contain species of *Mariella* having characteristics which anticipate the spiral groove of the common Cenomanian genus, *Plesioturrilites*. All these considerations suggest that the Pawpaw is at least *dispar-perinflatum* in age, and the uppermost beds may be in part Early Cenomanian.

Cenomanian. The Mainstreet contains species of *Ostlingoceras* and *Plesioturrilites* plus *Anisoceras perarmatum* which can be considered. This last species is common in the Late Albian zones, but the occurrence of species of *Ostlingoceras* and *Plesioturrilites* and certain regularly coiled ammonoids suggest that the formation is Cenomanian. Böse (1928, p. 152) compared regularly coiled species from the Mainstreet with Early Cenomanian species in Europe and concluded that *Mariella (Plesioturrilites) brazoensis,* the common Mainstreet species, was a good Early Cenomanian guide-fossil. This has been widely accepted (*e.g.,* Arkell and others, 1957, p. L222) but the occurrence of this species in the Weno (this report) indicates that at least the early members of the *Plesioturrilites* group are Late Albian.

The Grayson and Del Rio formations of Texas contain *Sciponoceras baculoides* and two species of *Scaphites, S. bosquensis* and *S. subevolutus,* which are of some value in a heteromorph classification. *Sciponoceras baculoides* has long been considered a Late Vraconian and Early Cenomanian species (Pervinquière, 1907, p. 92; Böse, 1928, p. 158), and the two listed species of *Scaphites,* although peculiar to Texas rocks, evidently are of the same group of *Scaphites* which are common in Cenomanian rocks of Europe (Böse, 1928, p. 159; Wright and Wright, 1951). An Early Cenomanian (*varians*) age for the Del Rio-Grayson units seems justified.

The Buda Limestone and Boquillas Flags contain *Hypoturrilites tuberculatus, Turrilites (Turrilites) acutus,* and species of *Ostlingoceras*. The first two of these have been known for more than 100 years from the "gray-chalk" or Cenomanian of England (Sharpe, 1853). Recently, Wright and Wright (1951) have indicated that these species belong to the *varians* zone of the Cenomanian. Species of *Ostlingoceras* are common in this part of the Cenomanian as well (Wright and Wright, 1951; Arkell and others, 1957).

No species of heteromorphs conspecific with European forms have been

TABLE 1. STRATIGRAPHIC RANGE OF HETEROMORPH SPECIES IN THE TEXAS CRETACEOUS

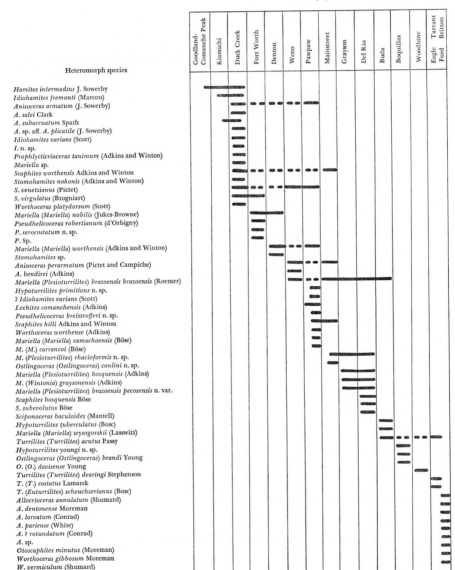

Texas stratigraphic units

Heteromorph species

Hamites intermedius J. Sowerby
Idiohamites fremonti (Marcou)
Anisoceras armatum (J. Sowerby)
A. salei Clark
A. subarcuatum Spath
A. sp. aff. A. plicatile (J. Sowerby)
Idiohamites varians (Scott)
I. n. sp.
Prophlycticrioceras tanimum (Adkins and Winton)
Mariella sp.
Scaphites worthensis Adkins and Winton
Stomohamites nokonis (Adkins and Winton)
S. venetzianus (Pictet)
S. virgulatus (Brogniart)
Worthoceras platydorsum (Scott)
Mariella (Mariella) nobilis (Jukes-Browne)
Pseudhelicoceras robertianum (d'Orbigny)
P. serocostatum n. sp.
P. Sp.
Mariella (Mariella) worthensis (Adkins and Winton)
Stomohamites sp.
Anisoceras perarmatum (Pictet and Campiche)
A. bendirei (Adkins)
Mariella (Plesioturrilites) brazoensis brazoensis (Roemer)
Hypoturrilites primitivus n. sp.
? Idiohamites varians (Scott)
Lechites comanchensis (Adkins)
Pseudhelicoceras breistrofferi n. sp.
Scaphites hilli Adkins and Winton
Worthoceras worthense (Adkins)
Mariella (Mariella) camachoensis (Böse)
M. (M.) carrancoi (Böse)
M. (Plesioturrilites) rhacioformis n. sp.
Ostlingoceras (Ostlingoceras) conlini n. sp.
Mariella (Plesioturrilites) bosquensis (Adkins)
M. (Wintonia) graysonensis (Adkins)
Mariella (Plesioturrilites) brazoensis pecosensis n. var.
Scaphites bosquensis Böse
S. subevolutus Böse
Sciponoceras baculoides (Mantell)
Hypoturrilites tuberculatus (Bosc)
Mariella (Mariella) wysogorskii (Lasswitz)
Turrilites (Turrilites) acutus Passy
Hypoturrilites youngi n. sp.
Ostlingoceras (Ostlingoceras) brandi Young
O. (O.) davisense Young
Turrilites (Turrilites) dearingi Stephenson
T. (T.) costatus Lamarck
T. (Euturrilites) scheuchzerianus (Bosc)
Allocrioceras annulatum (Shumard)
A. dentonense Moreman
A. larvatum (Conrad)
A. pariense (White)
A. ? rotundatum (Conrad)
A. sp.
Otoscaphites minutus (Moreman)
Worthoceras gibbosum Moreman
W. vermiculum (Shumard)

found in the Woodbine, but on the basis of regularly coiled forms the Woodbine has been considered Late Cenomanian (Stephenson, 1952, p. 17–35). Its
stratigraphic position above definite *varians* species and below definite
plenus species of the Turonian, indicates that it would correspond with the
subglobosus zone of the Cenomanian.

Cenomanian-Turonian. The Eagle Ford contains *Turrilites* (*Turrilites*)
costatus, T. (*T.*) *acutus,* and *T.* (*Euturrilites*) *scheuchzerianus* in the lower
part (Tarrant), all of which belong to the Late Cenomanian *subglobosus*
zone. The middle part of the Eagle Ford (Britton) contains species of *Allocrioceras* and *Worthoceras* which occur with the regularly coiled species
Metoicoceras whitei and *Kanabiceras septumseriatum* which belong to the
plenus or earliest zone of the Turonian (Arkell and others, 1957, p. L128;
Wright and Wright, 1951; Matsumoto, 1959, v. 2, p. 102). The Eagle Ford
Shale is Late Cenomanian in the lower part and Early Turonian in the middle part.

Loeblich and Tappan (1961) have challenged the Turonian age of the
Eagle Ford and have based their case on the absence of exclusively Turonian
planktonic Foraminifera. They consider the entire Eagle Ford to be Cenomanian. Recently, Swensen (1963) has summarized the evidence for a Turonian age for at least the middle and upper part of the Eagle Ford.

FACTORS IN EVOLUTION

Details of evolution of species are often more easily detected when a large sampling of a fossil population is available. Those collections from Texas which consist of several dozen to more than 1000 individuals exhibit excellent evolutionary patterns which can best be explained by consideration of the relationships between embryologic growth and evolution.

A synthesis of embryologic development and evolution has been published by De Beer (1958), and some of the details of this evolution among various Texas heteromorph species have recently been summarized (Clark, 1962).

Three aspects of embryology and evolution have been noted: (1) paedomorphosis, the most common of the types noted in Texas material, is defined as the possession by mature organisms of characters which were present only in the young of an ancestor (De Beer, 1958, p. 63); (2) acceleration is defined as the appearance of a character in the early stages of a descendant which is present only in the late stages of ontogeny of an ancestor (De Beer, 1958, p. 104); (3) caenogenesis is the case in which distinct species resemble one another in their adult stage but are very unlike in early stages of development (De Beer, 1958, p. 40).

The average *Mariella (Plesioturrilites) brazoensis* possessed vertical ribbing on the youngest whorls and this ornamentation becomes distinctly tuberculate in the adult. Occurring with *P. brazoensis* in the Mainstreet and becoming more numerous than it in the upper Grayson is a smaller form which is usually considered a variant of *P. brazoensis* but which differs in possessing distinct ribbing in all ontogenetic stages. This form is referred to *P. rhacioformis* n. sp. and seems to be an excellent example of paedomorphosis.

This same pattern has been noted in *Mariella (Mariella) worthensis* and *M. (Plesioturrilites) bosquensis*. In both species the average individual of the sampled population has small, slightly oblique nodes in the juvenile stages and larger rounded tubercules in the adult. The paedomorphic variety in both retains the juvenile characteristic in all stages of ontogeny. In *M. (M.) worthensis* this phenomenon occurs in about three per cent of 1200 specimens studied and in *M. (P.) bosquensis,* about two per cent of 1300 specimens.

In the *M. (M.) worthensis* population about two per cent acquire large distinct tubercles at an early stage of development. This condition is attained in about 80 per cent of the sample only at maturity and in the two per cent studied represents an example of acceleration.

Caenogenesis is well illustrated by *M. (P.) bosquensis* and *M. (Wintonia) graysonensis*. Adult shells of these two species cannot be distinguished, but in the earliest ontogenetic stage *Wintonia graysonensis* has at least one straight shaft. This shaft merges with a normally helically coiled shell during early ontogeny and a normally coiled shell results by maturity—the same shape and ornamented shell present in all stages of *Plesioturrilites bosquensis*. These species occur in the same stratigraphic interval and when the delicate straight shaft of *Wintonia* is broken (as it evidently is in most specimens) the two adult species cannot be distinguished even by discriminating statistical study.

Similar evolutionary factors are probably present in most of the species of heteromorphs studied but are not apparent because of the small sample of most species.

SYSTEMATIC PALEONTOLOGY

The following symbols are used to designate repositories:

BEG = Bureau of Economic Geology, University of Texas, Austin.

BYU = Paleontology Repository, Brigham Young University, Provo, Utah.

Conlin = J. P. Conlin Collection, 3617 Baldwin Street, Ft. Worth 10, Texas (to be deposited in U.S. National Museum).

IGM = Instituto Geologico Mexico, Mexico City, D.F.

TCU = Department of Geology, Texas Christian University, Ft. Worth, Texas.

USNM = U.S. National Museum, Washington, D.C.

UT = Department of Geology, University of Texas, Austin.

SMU = Department of Geology, Southern Methodist University, Dallas.

Suborder LYTOCERATINA Hyatt, 1889
Superfamily TURRILITACEAE Meek, 1876
Family HAMITIDAE Hyatt, 1900

Members of this family are characterized by early whorls which are in a plane spiral or helical and several straight shafts. Ribbing is variable and no tubercles are present. Swensen (1963) has described members of this family in detail as a part of the present study.

Genus *Hamites* Parkinson, 1811

This generic name was formerly used for species occurring in the entire Cretaceous, and most straight heteromorphs have been referred to it in early work. As presently defined, *Hamites* includes species with an early helical coiling which terminate in several subparallel shafts with a range of Upper Aptian through Upper Albian (Arkell and others, 1957, p. L216).

Hamites intermedius J. Sowerby
(Fig. 3a; Pl. 1, figs. 10, 14)

Hamites intermedius J. SOWERBY, 1814, London, B. Meredith, v. 1, p. 139, Pl. LXII, figs. 4a,b; SPATH, 1941, Palaeont. Soc. London Mon., pt. 14, p. 630–634, Fig. 229a–g, m–p, Pl. LXX, figs. 19, 20, Pl. LXXI, figs. 3–6; SWENSEN, 1963, Brigham Young Univ. Geol. Studies, v. 9, pt. 2, p. 60–61, Pl. 1, figs. 10, 14
Hamites adkinsi SCOTT, 1928, Jour. Paleontology, v. 2, p. 116, 118, Pl. 16, figs. 10, 13; ADKINS, 1928, Univ. Texas Bull. 2838, p. 208

Scott's *Hamites adkinsi* (1928) differs only slightly from *H. intermedius* and is here considered a junior synonym. The writer does not consider *H. intermedius distincta* Spath to be sufficiently different from *H. intermedius* to warrant separation. Specimen consists of two straight limbs joined by 180-degree hook; ribs rounded, on adapical limb high, prominent, widely spaced, three ribs in length equal to diameter. On adapertural limb ribs less prominent, closely spaced, with five to six occurring in length equal to diameter. Some ribs discontinuous, branching across venter of both limbs; ribs effaced on dorsum. Whorl section compressed (Fig. 3a).

19

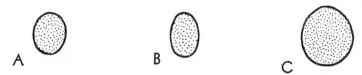

Figure 3. *Costal whorl sections, Family Hamitidae.* (A) *Hamites intermedius* ($\times$ 1); (B) *Stomohamites nokonis* ($\times$ 1); (C) *Stomohamites venetzianus* ($\times$ 3)

REMARKS: A single specimen from the Goodland-Comanche Peak was available for this study. One other specimen from the Duck Creek (TCU 1144) is questionably assigned to this species. It is an open hook-shaped specimen with rib spacing slightly different from the older specimen but with the same type inequalities present in the ribbing.

H. intermedius is similar to *H. maximas* J. Sowerby, but the former has a more compressed whorl section and a smooth dorsum. It differs from *H. subrotundus* Spath and *H. incurvatus* Brown by its whorl section and smooth dorsum and from *Stomohamites funatus* by its blunt ribs. Böse (1923, Pl. 9, figs. 46–49) figured a specimen with affinities to *H. intermedius* from the Vraconian of Mexico.

OCCURRENCE: *H. intermedius* occurs at the top of the Middle Albian *cristatum* subzone of the Lower Gault and extends into the Upper Albian *orbignyi* and *varicosum* subzones as well. The Texas specimen (= *H. adkinsi* Scott) is from the middle of the Comanche Peak Limestone near Valley Mills, Texas.

REPOSITORY: TCU 1046

Genus *Stomohamites* Breistroffer, 1940

"Typically with denser ribs than *Hamites* and at least some species have strongly collared and constricted aperture; venter tends to be flat. Suture with 3rd lateral saddle nearly as big as others and symmetrically bifid. U. Alb.—L. Turon." (Arkell and others, 1957, p. L217).

Swensen (1963) has pointed out that the Texas species of *Stomohamites* do not have a venter which is as flat as the average European forms.

Stomohamites nokonis (Adkins and Winton)
(Fig. 3b; Pl. 1, fig. 11; Pl. 2, fig. 14)

Hamites sp. B, WINTON AND ADKINS, 1920, Univ. Texas Bull. 1931, p. 23
Hamites nokonis ADKINS AND WINTON, 1920, Univ. Texas Bull. 1945, p. 18, 39–40, Pl. 6, figs. 5, 6; WINTON AND ADKINS, 1920, Univ. Texas Bull. 1931, p. 22; SCOTT, 1926, Univ. Grenoble Thèse, Faculty Sci., p. 65; ADKINS, 1928, Univ. Texas Bull. 2838, p. 19, 208, Pl. 12, fig. 2; PERKINS, 1961, Geol. Soc. America Mem. 83, p. 27
Stomohamites nokonis SWENSEN, 1963, Brigham Young Univ. Geol. Studies, v. 9, pt. 2, p. 62–63, Pl. 2, fig. 14

Straight shaft, compressed whorl section (Fig. 3b), numerous closely spaced ribs, seven to eight in length equal to diameter. Ribs low, widest around venter, absent or faint on dorsum. Shape and inclination variable.

REMARKS: Stratigraphic position, compressed whorl section, and closely spaced ribs distinguish this species from *S. venetzianus* (Pictet) and *S. virgulatus* (Brongniart), the only other known species in the Texas Cretaceous. Swensen (1963) has pointed out that these same features distinguish *S. nokonis* from the related species *S. duplicatus* (Pictet and Campiche), *S. charpentieri* (Pictet), *S. ptychoceratoides* Spath, *Hamites compressus* J. Sowerby, and *H. gardneri* Spath. These latter two species have ribs prominent across the dorsum.

OCCURRENCE: *S. nokonis* occurs with *Idiohamites fremonti* (Marcou) at the base of the Duck Creek Formation in southern Oklahoma to central Texas. The holotype was collected from the military road cut, half a mile north of Texas Christian University, in Ft. Worth, Texas.

REPOSITORY: BEG 20984; USNM 131910

Stomohamites venetzianus (Pictet)
(Figs. 3c, 4; Pl. 1, figs. 1–6)

Hamites venetzianus PICTET, *in* PICTET AND ROUX, 1847, Soc. Physics Histoire Nat. Genève Mèm. 11, pt. 2, p. 134, Pl. XIV, fig. 6
Hamites (Stomohamites) venetzianus SPATH, 1941, Palaeont. Soc. London Mon., pt. 14, p. 638–640, Fig. 231, Pl. LXXI, figs. 11–13
Hamites tenawa ADKINS AND WINTON, 1920, Univ. Texas Bull. 1945, p. 28, 43–44, Pl. 6, fig. 4; WINTON AND ADKINS, 1920, Univ. Texas Bull. 1931, p. 21; ADKINS, 1920, Univ. Texas Bull. 1856, p. 38, 51, 67, 69; SCOTT, 1924, Texas Christian Univ. Quart., v. 1, p. 15, 17; SCOTT, 1926, Univ. Grenoble Thèse Faculty Sci., p. 80; ADKINS, 1928, Univ. Texas Bull. 2838, p. 24, 208, 210, Pl. 20, fig. 14; BÖSE, 1928, Univ. Texas Bull. 2748, p. 146
Hamites sp. WINTON AND ADKINS, 1920, Univ. Texas Bull. 1931, p. 69
Stomohamites venetzianus SWENSEN, 1963, Brigham Young Univ. Geol. Studies, v. 9, pt. 2, p. 64, Pl. 1, figs. 1–6

Short, gently curved shaft, compressed to circular whorl section (Fig. 3c), blunt oblique ribs. Ribs prominent, simple, rounded, widest across venter; four in length equal to diameter; faint or absent across dorsum. Suture (Fig. 4) less oblique second lateral lobe than that illustrated by Spath (1941).

Figure 4. *Suture of* Stomohamites venetzianus (4 mm, × 4.5)

REMARKS: *Hamites tenawa* Adkins and Winton (1920) differs only slightly in rib spacing and is regarded as a junior synonym of *S. venetzianus* (Swensen, 1963). This species is similar to *S. virgulatus* and *S. subvirgulatus* except for its blunt, widely spaced, oblique ribs.

OCCURRENCE: *S. venetzianus* occurs in the basal Pawpaw Formation in the Ft. Worth area of north Texas. One specimen tentatively assigned to this species is from Duck Creek Formation near Denison, Texas. Böse (1923, Pl. 9, figs. 50–53) figured a specimen with affinities to *S. venetzianus* from the Vraconian of northern Mexico. This species occurs in the *aequatorialis* to *substuderi* subzones of the English Gault.

REPOSITORY: BEG 20988 (= *Hamites tenawa*, holotype); TCU 1142; 1143

Stomohamites virgulatus (Brongniart)
(Fig. 5; Pl. 1, fig. 13; Pl. 2, fig. 15)

Hamites virgulatus BRONGNIART, *in* CUVIER AND BRONGNIART, 1822, Paris, Pl. O, fig. 6; ADKINS, 1920, Univ. Texas Bull. 1856, p. 66; ADKINS AND WINTON, 1920, Univ. Texas Bull. 1945, p. 43
Hamites (Stomohamites) virgulatus SPATH, 1941, Palaeont. Soc. London Mon., pt. 14, p. 635–638, Fig. 230, Pl. LXXI, figs. 7–10; Pl. LXXII, fig. 11
Stomohamites virgulatus WRIGHT, *in* ARKELL, KUMMEL, AND WRIGHT, 1957, *Treatise on Invertebrate Paleontology* (Moore, R. C., *Editor*): Geol. Soc. America and Univ. Kansas Press, pt. L, p. L217; SWENSEN, 1963, Brigham Young Univ. Geol. Studies, v. 9, pt. 2, p. 65–66, Pl. 1, fig. 13, Pl. 2, fig. 15

"Coiling probably more or less anisoceratid, without sudden bends, but often slightly helicoid; whorl-section compressed oval to almost circular. Ribs sharp, straight, effaced on smooth dorsum and not very closely spaced." (Spath, 1941, p. 636)

Texas specimens prominent ribs across venter, simple, straight; dorsum smooth; whorl section slightly more compressed than European material.

REMARKS: Swensen (1963) differentiated *S. virgulatus* from *S. subvirgulatus* Spath and

S. parkinsoni (Fleming) by its less closely spaced ribs and from *S. venetzianus* and *S. nokonis* by its sharp straight ribs and whorl shape (Fig. 5). Two specimens (Conlin 5755, 8442) from

Figure 5. *Costal whorl section of* Stomohamites virgulatus (× 1)

the Fort Worth Formation have affinities with *S. virgulatus* but have more rounded ribs and a more circular whorl section.

OCCURRENCE: Duck Creek and Fort Worth Formations in north Texas. The species occurs in the *aequatorialis* and *substuderi* subzones of the English Gault. This is higher stratigraphically than the Texas material and the specimens so identified may represent a variety of the type material.

REPOSITORY: BEG 35366; UT 689

Family BACULITIDAE Meek, 1876

This ubiquitous group of heteromorphs includes only six genera (Arkell and others, 1957, p. L218); however, the number of individuals belonging to this family is legend.

Two "primitive" genera, *Lechites* and *Sciponoceras* appeared first in the Late Albian. By Late Cretaceous the species of the more advanced genera were abundant throughout the world. Both of the early genera are present in the Albian-Cenomanian sequence in Texas although neither are abundant in rocks of this age. Only a single species of each genus is presently known in Texas.

The very abundant Upper Cretaceous Baculitidae have been the subject of numerous publications in this country and abroad. The value of species of baculitids in biostratigraphy is well known, and recently Cobban (1958a; 1958b) has utilized species in the Western Interior. Evidently, baculitids are more abundant in the Western Interior Cretaceous than in the equivalent Texas rocks, even though there were connections of seas in these two areas during parts of the Cretaceous.

Students of the baculitids have used the characters of the aperture for classification on the generic and specific level; so those individuals on which apertures are not preserved are difficult to classify. Unfortunately, all Albian and Cenomanian baculitids from Texas available for this study lack the apertures. Furthermore, none of the Texas species have ever been described with the body chamber complete. Features of ornamentation and whorl shape have been used for the Texas material, but this is not completely satisfactory.

Species of this group possess a straight or slightly curved shaft which follows a small initial coiled portion. Ornamentation consists of swelling or tubercles and small ribs.

Only the Albian and Cenomanian species of this family are described in this report. Other species from younger stratigraphic units in the Texas Cretaceous include:

Baculites annulatus Shumard, *B. gracilus* Shumard, and *B.* sp. aff. *B. gracilus,* from the Eagle Ford;

Baculites anceps Lamarck, *B. asper* Morton, and *B. asepero-anceps* Lasswitz, from the Austin;

B. taylorensis Adkins and *B. ovatus* Say, from the Taylor;

B. claviformis Stephenson, *B. columna* Morton, and *B. undatus* Stephenson, from the Navarro.

Genus *Lechites* Nowak, 1908

Genus characterized by ". . . section circular or oval, without constrictions; regular low prorsiradiate ribs . . ." may be present (Arkell and others, 1957, p. L218).

Spath (1941) has pointed out that the lack of constrictions and the differences in apertures are the chief distinguishing features between this genus and *Sciponoceras*.

Typical *Lechites* have an aperture turned toward the dorsum with a simple collar and fine ribs. This genus is known to range from the Late Albian into the Early Cenomanian.

Lechites comanchensis (Adkins)
(Fig. 6a; Pl. 3, figs. 1, 2, 5–11; Pl. 4, fig. 16)

Baculites sp. WINTON AND ADKINS, 1920, Univ. Texas Bull. 1931, p. 21, 69
Baculites comanchensis ADKINS, 1920, Univ. Texas Bull. 1856, p. 51, 74–76, Pl. 2, figs. 20–22;
  ADKINS, 1928, Univ. Texas Bull. 2838, p. 23; BÖSE, 1928, Univ. Texas Bull. 2748, p. 146
Cyrtochilus (?) *comanchensis* ADKINS, 1928, Univ. Texas Bull. 2838, p. 207, Pl. 20, fig. 9;
  SPATH, 1941, Palaeont. Soc. London Mon., pt. 14, p. 666

Only a few specimens of this species are known to the writer. All consist of phragmocone only, and hence the understanding of this species is only partially satisfactory. Adkins' original description (1920, p. 74–75) was based on only a few individuals from the Pawpaw Formation, and he mentioned that the species was rare. In the most recent monograph of the Texas Washita formations, Perkins (1961) does not mention this species in a discussion of the Pawpaw. The observations recorded here are based on six incomplete specimens obtained from the Bureau of Economic Geology collections at Austin.

Adkins' description (1920, p. 74–75) follows:

". . . cross-section a short oval; living (body) chamber not preserved, but sutures suddenly more crowded at larger end. Ribs consist of evenly rounded, low, annular swellings in a plane nearly perpendicular to the long axis of the shell, . . . they turn sharply toward the . . . (adapical) end of the shell and become obsolete upon crossing the dorsum."

REMARKS: The nature of the ribbing and the suture are about the only characters which can be used to advantage in studying this species; based on these characters this species is considered to belong to the genus *Lechites*. Adkins (1928, p. 207), 8 years after describing this species, considered that it might possibly belong to *Cyrtochilus* (= *Sciponoceras*), but Spath (1941) thought that it was closer to *Lechites, L. moreti,* and *L. gaudini* in particular. This same writer (p. 666) indicated that on species of *Lechites* the ribs are effaced on the dorsum, whereas on species of *Sciponoceras* the ribs are continuous on the dorsum. Also, he mentioned (p. 661) that ". . . the presence of constrictions in *Cyrtochilus* (= *Sciponoceras*), and the difference in the aperture are more important distinctions."

Lechites comanchensis can be distinguished from *L. moreti* and *L. gaudini* by the possession of straight ribs which turn toward the apical end, swell, and terminate on the dorsum. *L. communis* Spath has much different and more closely spaced ribs than *L. comanchensis*. The individual referred to as *Baculites* cfr. *gaudini* by Böse (1928, Pl. 10, figs. 66–74) has quite oblique ribs. The suture of *L. comanchensis* (Fig. 6a) is somewhat similar to the

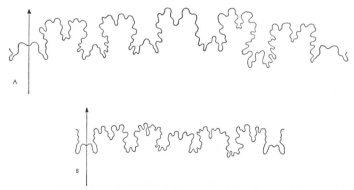

Figure 6. *Sutures, Family Baculitidae.* (A) *Lechites comanchensis* (4 mm, × 4.5); (B) *Sciponoceras baculoides* (5 mm, × 4.5)

various sutures figured by Spath (1941, Figs. 242, 243) and agrees with his observations that the suture of species of *Lechites* are more simple and have a smaller second lateral lobe than principal lobe, as compared with sutures of *Sciponoceras*.

OCCURRENCE: From the basal beds of the Pawpaw (Late Albian *dispar-perinflatum*). Adkins' localities 714 and 719, one-quarter mile south of the International and Great

Northern Railway Bridge across Sycamore Creek, 4½ miles Southeast of Ft. Worth, Texas; and 1 mile south of Baptist Seminary on Crowley Road, 4½ miles south of Ft. Worth.

REPOSITORY: BEG 20997 (holotype); 20998, 20999 (paratypes). Specimens also in the museum of TCU and in collections of USNM.

Genus *Sciponoceras* Hyatt, 1894

This genus is characterized by strong prorsiradiate constrictions and an aperture turned toward the dorsum with strong broad folds and a more elaborate suture than in *Lechites*. Species of this genus range from the Late Albian into the Late Turonian and occur worldwide. Only a single species from the Texas Cretaceous is known.

Sciponoceras baculoides (Mantell)
(Fig. 6b; Pl. 3, figs. 3, 4, 12, 13)

Baculites baculoides BÖSE, 1923, Geol. Inst. Mexico Bol., v. 42, p. 156, Pl. 10, figs. 75–81
Baculites cfr. *baculoides* BÖSE, 1928, Univ. Texas Bull. 2748, p. 154, 158, 210–211, Pl. 3, figs. 11–14, Pl. 4, figs. 3–11
Baculites cfr. *comanchensis* ADKINS, 1928, Univ. Texas Bull. 2838, p. 25
Cyrtochilus aff. *baculoides* ADKINS, 1928, Univ. Texas Bull. 2838, p. 207

The above synonymy traces the variations in generic and specific assignments of this species, but it should be emphasized that by 1928 Adkins thought that the Del Rio *S. baculoides* was conspecific with the Pawpaw *Lechites comanchensis* (1928, p. 25, 207). However, Böse (1928) also indicated that he could not distinguish the Del Rio species from *B. baculoides*.

All known Texas specimens are small, with a slightly compressed whorl section and conspicuous prorsiradiate constrictions. Other ornamentation noted consists of weak prorsiradiate ribs. Presence of constrictions on *S. baculoides* and their absence on *L. comanchensis* distinguish the two species. In addition, *L. comanchensis* bears straight ribs which are absent on *S. baculoides*. Suture is illustrated (Fig. 6b).

OCCURRENCE: This species is widespread in the Cenomanian rocks of Africa and Europe. In Texas it occurs in the Del Rio, Böse's localities 964 and 966 (1928) on the east bank of South Bosque River, 2 miles south of South Bosque, near Bickle no. 2 well; and on the east side of Sante Fe track, 4½ miles southeast of McGregor, McLennan County, Texas. Böse (1923, p. 156) reported that the species ". . . se encuentra con mucha freuencia . . ." in the region of Camacho, Mexico.

REPOSITORY: BEG 21036, 21037, 18785

Family ANISOCERATIDAE Hyatt, 1900

This family has been described recently by Swensen (1963), who reported 16 species from the Texas Cretaceous. The family consists of species which are loosely coiled, helical in the early stages, normally followed by a series of straight shafts which occur in one plane. Ventral and lateral tubercles are commonly present. Arkell and others (1957, p. L218) consider this group a monophyletic family derived from the Hamitidae. Representatives of this family are found from the Lower Albian through the Upper Turonian.

Genus *Anisoceras* Pictet, 1854

Species of this genus coil helically in the young stages and have one or two straight shafts. Ventral and lateral tubercles are commonly present. Members of this genus are present from the Upper Albian to the Upper Turonian. Adkins (1931) reported Turonian *Anisoceras* from west Texas, and the writer collected several specimens from Adkins' Chispa Summit locality which could not be specifically identified. Young (1963, p. 44–45) has described these as a species of *Allocrioceras*.

Böse (1923) reported several species of *Anisoceras* from northern Mexico. The specimens are poorly preserved, small, and the various species assignments do not seem to be justified, especially the new ones.

Anisoceras armatum (J. Sowerby)
(Fig. 7a; Pl. 5, fig. 4; Pl. 6, fig. 6)

Hamites armatus J. SOWERBY, 1817, London, B. Meredith, v. 2, p. 153, Pl. CLXVIII; ADKINS, 1920, Univ. Texas Bull. 1856, p. 66–67; SCOTT, 1924, Texas Christian Univ. Quart., v. 1, p. 15,17; ADKINS, 1928, Univ. Texas Bull. 2838, p. 24
Hamites sp. aff. *H. armatus* ADKINS, 1920, Univ. Texas Bull. 1856, p. 51, 69–70; SCOTT, 1926, Univ. Grenoble Thèse, Faculty Sci., p. 80; BÖSE, 1928, Univ. Texas Bull. 2748, p. 146; ADKINS, 1928, Univ. Texas Bull. 2838, p. 24
Anisoceras armatum SPATH, 1939, Palaeont. Soc. London Mon., pt. 13, p. 543–548, Fig. 191, Pl. LIX, fig. 6, Pl. LX, fig. 1, Pl. LXI, figs. 9–11, Pl. LXII, fig. 5; SWENSEN, 1963, Brigham Young Univ. Geol. Studies, v. 9, pt. 2, p. 66–67, Pl. 3, fig. 4, Pl. 4, fig. 6
Anisoceras cfr. *armatum* BÖSE, 1923, Geol. Inst. Mexico Bol., v. 42, p. 143, Pl. 10, figs. 22–24
Anisoceras sp. aff. *A. armatum* ADKINS, 1928, Univ. Texas Bull. 2838, p. 211
Anisoceras cf. *A. armatum* CLARK, 1958, Jour. Paleontology, v. 32, p. 1080, Pl. 139, fig. 2

Spath (1939, p. 545) described the species:

"Coiling anisoceratid. Whorl-section cylindrical or slightly compressed, with scarcely flattened sides and rather narrow venter. Small lateral tubercles below middle of the whorl-side; generally one or two intermediate ribs. Less regularity on the final shaft."

REMARKS: Böse (1923) referred specimens to *A. armatum* which are completely recrystallized and not identifiable specifically. They are of the general type of *A. armatum* but consist of early helical portion which is difficult to distinguish specifically. Spath (1939) has discussed the difficulties of separating juvenile *A. armatum* from *A. saussureanum* (Pictet). Also, *A. perarmatum* Pictet and Campiche has one or two nontuberculate intermediate ribs in early stages, making it similar to both *A. armatum* and *A. saussureanum*. Swensen (1963) described several specimens which vary slightly from the type, including one specimen that had no looping of ribs.

The whorl section of the Texas specimens is nearly cylindrical to laterally compressed (Fig. 7a).

A   B   C

Figure 7. *Whorl sections, Family Anisoceratidae.* (A) Costal whorl section of *Anisoceras armatum* (× 2); (B) Costal whorl section of *Anisoceras bendirei* (× 1); (C) Intercostal whorl section of *Anisoceras* sp. aff. *A. plicatile* (× 1)

OCCURRENCE: In Texas, *A. armatum* occurs in the Duck Creek, and Pawpaw Formations. One large specimen from Medina County is from an unknown horizon. Adkins (1920, p. 69) mentioned specimens from the basal third of the Pawpaw Formation at his locality 714. J. P. Conlin has several specimens from this locality.

In England, this species occurs in the *?auritus-dispar* subzones of the Gault.

REPOSITORY: BEG 35362, 35363, 35364

Anisoceras perarmatum Pictet and Campiche
(Pl. 6, figs. 1, 3, 7)

Anisoceras perarmatum PICTET AND CAMPICHE, 1861, Paléont. Suisse, v. 2, no. 2, p. 65, Pl. XLVIII, figs. 7, 8, Pl. XLIX, figs. 1, 2–8; SCOTT, 1926, Univ. Grenoble Thèse, Faculty Sci., p. 61–62; SPATH, 1939, Palaeont. Soc. London Mon., pt. 13, p. 548–550, Fig. 192, Pl. LIX, figs. 1–3, Pl. LXI, figs. 3–7; SWENSEN, 1963, Brigham Young Univ. Geol. Studies, v. 9, pt. 2, p. 67–68, Pl. 4, figs. 1, 3, 7

"Coiling anisoceratid, with twist of early whorls often inconspicuous. Whorl-section hexagonal, sometimes slightly depressed on straight shafts or on bend. Ribbing first as in other *Anisoceras*, with one or even two fine intermediary ribs between the pronounced and quadrituberculate main ribs, but these soon increase in strength and all the intermediate ribs are lost. Irregular ornamentation on final portion. Tubercles connected by loops on venter and sides. Dorsum almost smooth." (Spath, 1939, p. 549)

The Texas specimens of this species are all poorly preserved, but the strong looping caused by the bridging of tubercles by parallel ribs is here considered diagnostic.

REMARKS: Swensen (1963) described one specimen from the Texas Cretaceous which shows injury during life. The body chamber has alternating tubercles on the venter and is quite similar to specimens of the same species observed by the writer in the Geological Survey Museum, London, (e.g., no. 69797) and in the collections of C. W. Wright (London).

This species differs from others by the consistency of loops and the lack of intermediate nontuberculate ribs on the larger portions of the phragmocone.

OCCURRENCE: TCU 1140 was collected from the Weno Formation near Rio Vista, Texas. BEG 35373 is from the Weno Formation of an unknown locality. Poorly preserved specimens are known in the Mainstreet Formation. English specimens occur in the *aequatorialis-dispar* subzones of the Gault.

REPOSITORY: TCU 1140; BEG 35373

Anisoceras bendirei (Adkins)
(Fig. 7b; Pl. 5, figs. 6–8, 11)

Hamites sp. B. WINTON AND ADKINS, 1920, Univ. Texas Bull. 1931, p. 22

Ancyloceras bendirei ADKINS, 1920, Univ. Texas Bull. 1856, p. 8, 48, 70–71, 103, 125, 137, 142, Pl. 11, fig. 1; SCOTT, 1926, Univ. Grenoble Thèse, Faculty Sci., p. 74, 76, 190

Ancyloceras bendirei BÖSE, 1928, Univ. Texas Bull. 2748, p. 146; ADKINS, 1928, Univ. Texas Bull. 2838, p. 21, 216

Anisoceras bendirei CLARK, 1958, Jour. Paleontology, v. 32, p. 1077–1079, Pl. 140, figs. 1, 2; SWENSEN, 1963, Brigham Young Univ. Geol. Studies, v. 9, pt. 2, p. 68–69, Pl. 3, figs. 6–8, 11

Hexagonal whorl shape (Fig. 7b), spinose tubercles, wide flat venter; one or two nontuberculate ribs cross venter between bituberculate ribs; two to three fine intermediate ribs on dorsum. Occasionally, ribs contact prominent tubercles on either side which results in looping effect, as in *A. perarmatum*. Tubercles larger on venter than on mid-lateral position; ribs bearing these faint to absent below mid-lateral tubercle position.

REMARKS: Swensen (1963) broadened the description of this species, basing his study on more specimens than were available to previous workers. *A. bendirei* is distinct from *A. saussureanum* and *A. perarmatum* by its intermediate ribs which extend across the dorsum and its more rounded, hexagonal whorl shape and mid-lateral position of the tubercles. Clark (1958) and Swensen (1963) have discussed this species in some detail.

OCCURRENCE: The holotype is from the basal Weno, 10 feet above the Denton, Ft. Worth, Texas. Numerous individuals of this species, all from the Weno, have been studied in the collections of the Bureau of Economic Geology, Austin, in the J. P. Conlin collection, Ft. Worth, and in the Renfro and other collections of the U.S. National Museum.

REPOSITORY: BEG 20271 (holotype), 21133; TCU 1138, 1139

Anisoceras salei Clark
(Pl. 6, fig. 4)

Anisoceras sp. SALE, 1957, M. A. thesis, Texas Christian Univ., p. ii, 33–34, 92, Pls. 18, 19

Anisoceras salei CLARK, 1958, Jour. Paleontology, v. 32, p. 1079–1080, Pl. 140, fig. 3; SWENSEN, 1963, Brigham Young Univ. Geol. Studies, v. 9, pt. 2, p. 69–70, Pl. 4, fig. 4

"Heavy tubercle-bearing ribs are separated by four to six intermediate fine ribs on the main shaft. This shaft is connected by a 180 degree hook to a smaller straight shaft, the adapical portion. On the smaller shaft there are two intermediate ribs. The ribs are slightly oblique on the hook to vertical on the shafts. Two rows of ventral and lateral tubercles are present, a pair of each on every heavy rib. The ventral tubercles are large and . . . the lateral tubercles are the larger . . . situated below the middle of the whorl side. The tubercles on the final shaft are between 35–43 mm. apart and average less than 38 mm. The whorl shape is highly compressed." (Clark, 1958)

REMARKS: *A. salei* is most similar to *A. armatum* and *A. saussureanum*. *A. salei* has more intermediate ribs than the former and is more compressed and has more widely spaced tubercles than the latter. These rather fine differences serve to distinguish the species presently, but additional material may indicate that the variations here noted could be included in *A. saussureanum*.

This is the largest-size known Texas *Anisoceras*.

OCCURRENCE: Holotype is from 20 feet above the base of the Duck Creek in southwest Ft. Worth, Texas. BEG 17398 is from the Duck Creek (?) south of Belton, Texas; Conlin 8323 is from the Duck Creek at the junction of Highway 80 and 377 in Arlington Heights; and BEG 21135 is from an unknown locality in the Duck Creek. These are the presently known specimens.

REPOSITORY: SMU 35003 (holotype); BEG 17398, 21135; Conlin 8323

Anisoceras sp. aff. *A. plicatile* (J. Sowerby)
(Fig. 7c; Pl. 1, figs. 15, 16)

Anisoceras sp. aff. *A. plicatile* SWENSEN, 1963, Brigham Young Univ. Geol. Studies, v. 9, pt. 2, p. 70–71, Pl. 1, figs. 15, 16

Small curved fragment from helical coiled part with heavy tubercle-bearing ribs separated by fine continuous intermediates only slightly less distinct on dorsum. Tubercles flattened, contact several ribs. Highly compressed whorl section (Fig. 7c), venter on lateral side.

REMARKS: The specimen here referred to differs from *A. plicatile* principally by its compressed helical whorl section, which may not be diagnostic at an early stage. The helical fragment illustrated by Schlüter (1876, Pl. 34, figs. 6–8) is hexagonal, however, and Spath (1939, p. 557) indicates the age of *A. plicatile* as Cenomanian. The Texas specimen is from the Upper Albian.

OCCURRENCE: Upper Duck Creek (Ft. Worth?) in creek bed at the southeast corner of Forest Park, Ft. Worth, Texas.

REPOSITORY: TCU 1141

Anisoceras subarcuatum Spath
(Fig. 8a; Pl. 6, figs. 2, 5)

Anisoceras subarcuatum SPATH, 1939, Palaeont. Soc. London Mon., pt. 13, p. 560–562, Fig. 198, Pl. LXII, fig. 5; Pl. XLV, fig. 1; Pl. LXVI, fig. 1
Anisoceras sp. aff. *A. subarcuatum* SWENSEN, 1963, Brigham Young Univ. Geol. Studies, v. 9, pt. 2, p. 71–72, Pl. 4, figs. 2, 5

Swensen (1963) referred, with some question, a single specimen to this species. The specimen consists of a straight shaft and a part of a 180-degree hook and has characteristics of both *Anisoceras* and *Idiohamites*.

Compressed whorl section, narrow venter, very strong tubercles on heavy ribs bifurcate across dorsum. Swensen (1963) regarded the absence of two intermediate ribs on the Texas specimen as being critical for species identification, but intermediate ribs do occur on either end of the specimen which is poorly preserved. Also, the ribbing is slightly more widely spaced than on the English specimens. Ventral tubercles are the larger.

REMARKS: Spath (1939, p. 561) pointed out that this species was transitional between *Anisoceras* and *Idiohamites*.

"This species could well have been included in *Idiohamites* (*spiniger*) . . . on the one hand, and *Anisoceras armatum* . . . on the other. It is now referred to *Anisoceras* on account of its early twist and the robustness of the ornament . . ."

The compressed whorl section (Fig. 8a) and narrow venter are characteristics of *Idiohamites* but the four tubercles on strong ribs, which bifurcate on the dorsum, are features of *Anisoceras*.

OCCURRENCE: The single specimen of this species available for this study is from the Kiamichi or Duck Creek Formation in Grayson County, near Fink. English specimens are from the *varicosum-auritus* subzones of the Gault.

REPOSITORY: BEG 35365

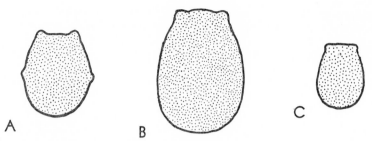

Figure 8. *Costal whorl sections, Family Anisoceratidae.* (A) *Anisoceras subarcuatum* (× 1); (B) *Idiohamites fremonti* (× 1); (C) *Idiohamites varians* (× 3)

Genus *Idiohamites* Spath, 1925

Members of this genus are among the most common of the heteromorphs which can be collected from the Texas Cretaceous presently. Arkell and others (1957, p. L220) have described the genus as follows:

"Coiling rather irregular, in one plane; ribs straight or oblique, with pair of ventral tubercles, joined only by single ribs on venter; lateral tubercles rarely present."

Species are found from the Upper Albian through the Cenomanian.

Idiohamites fremonti (Marcou)
(Fig. 8b; Pl. 5, figs. 5, 9; Pl. 7, figs. 1–7)

Hamites fremonti MARCOU, 1858, Zurich, Zürcher and Furrer, Pl. 1, fig. 3; SHUMARD, 1860, Acad. Sci. St. Louis Trans., v. 1, no. 4, p. 583, 587; HILL, 1891, Geol. Soc. America Bull., v. 2, p. 516; BOYLE, 1893, U.S. Geol. Survey Bull. 102, p. 144; HYATT, 1894, Am. Philos. Soc. Proc., v. 32, p. 577; HILL, 1901, U.S. Geol. Survey 21st Ann. Rept., pt. 7, Pl. 35, fig. 3; WINTON AND ADKINS, 1920, Univ. Texas Bull., 1931, p. 23, 51; ADKINS AND WINTON, 1920, Univ. Texas Bull. 1945, p. 18, 38, 40–41, 73, Pl. 6, fig. 3; WINTON, 1925, Univ. Texas Bull. 2544, p. 20; SCOTT, 1926, Univ. Grenoble Thèse, Faculty Sci., p. 65; ADKINS, 1927, Univ. Texas Bull. 2738, p. 41, 44, 51, 53, 55, 63, 69, 72, Pl. 4, fig. 2; ADKINS, 1928, Univ. Texas Bull. 2838, p. 15, 17, 19, 208–209, 212, Pl. 6, fig. 2; ADKINS AND ARICK, 1930, Univ. Texas Bull. 3016, p. 43; BULLARD AND CUYLER, 1930, Univ. Texas Bull. 3001, p. 74; BULLARD, 1931, Univ. Texas Bull. 3125, p. 28; ADKINS, 1933, Univ. Texas Bull. 3232, p. 352, 355, 360, 368
Hamites fromenti SCOTT, 1926, Univ. Grenoble Thèse, Faculty Sci., p. 61
Hamites sp. ADKINS AND WINTON, 1920, Univ. Texas Bull. 1945, Pl. 6, fig. 3
Exiteloceras fremonti ADKINS, 1928, Univ. Texas Bull. 2838, p. 212
Idiohamites fremonti ADKINS, 1933, Univ. Texas Bull. 3232, p. 352, 363, 368; FERAY, 1949, Shreveport Geol. Soc. 17th Ann. Field Trip Guidebook, p. 31, Pl. 8; YOUNG, 1957, Jour. Paleontology, v. 31, p. 18; SHELBURNE, 1959, Univ. Texas Pub. 5905, p. 117, Pl. 38, fig. 4; YOUNG, 1959, Am. Jour. Sci., v. 257, p. 759–761; PERKINS, 1961, Geol. Soc. America Mem. 83, p. 27; SWENSEN, 1963, Brigham Young Univ. Geol. Studies, v. 9, pt. 2, p. 72–74, Pl. 2, fig. 11, Pl. 3, figs. 5, 9, Pl. 5, figs. 1–7
Hamites comanchensis ADKINS AND WINTON, 1920, Univ. Texas Bull. 1945, p. 13–15, 18–19, 21–23, 25, 38–39, 53, 73, Pl. 6, fig. 10; WINTON AND ADKINS, 1920, Univ. Texas Bull. 1931, p. 22; WINTON, 1925, Univ. Texas Bull. 2544, p. 20, 53, Pl. 6, fig. 5; SCOTT, 1926, Univ. Grenoble Thèse, Faculty Sci., p. 61, 65; ADKINS, 1927, Univ. Texas Bull. 2738, p. 41, 44, 51, 53, 55, 63, 65, 67–68, 70–72; ADKINS, 1928, Univ. Texas Bull. 2838, p. 15, 17, 19, 208–209, Pl. 12, fig. 4; CUYLER, 1929, Am. Assoc. Petroleum Geologists Bull., v. 13, p. 1297; ADKINS AND ARICK, 1930, Univ. Texas Bull. 3016, p. 43; ADKINS, 1933, Univ. Texas Bull. 3232, p. 352, 358; LOZO, 1943, Am. Assoc. Petroleum Geologists Bull., v. 27, p. 1070
Hamites sp. near *comanchensis* ADKINS AND WINTON, 1920, Univ. Texas Bull. 1945, Pl. 6, figs. 7–9
Hamites aff. *comancheanus* ADKINS, 1933, Univ. Texas Bull. 3232, p. 352

Idiohamites comanchensis ADKINS, 1933, Univ. Texas Bull. 3232, p. 353; PERKINS, 1961, Geol. Soc. America Mem. 83, p. 23, 25, 27, 42

Swensen (1963) made a comprehensive study of this species and determined that *I. comanchensis* is a junior synonym of the well known *I. fremonti,* which is widespread and an important marker of the basal Duck Creek Formation.

Whorl section compressed during early growth to only slightly compressed and then greatly compressed at maturity (Fig. 8b); ribs equal in size, prominent, rounded, extend equally strongly across venter and sides, faint on dorsum. Three to five ribs in length equal to diameter, slightly more dense on holotype. Tubercles on ventral margins, commonly below mid-lateral position as well. Ventral tubercles variable, some small sharp projections but more commonly large, rounded. They occur on every second or third rib, although some have as many as three nontuberculate ribs and some specimens have prominent tubercles on every rib. Lateral tubercles small, inconspicuous, occur as low as dorsolateral margins, prominent on better-preserved specimens. Venter narrow but flattened.

REMARKS: Swensen (1963, p. 73) studied more than 100 specimens of *I. fremonti* and *I. comanchensis* including holotypes of both and concluded

". . . that there were no characteristics sufficiently distinct among the specimens to warrant a species distinction and *I. comanchensis* is regarded as a junior synonym of *I. fremonti.* The variability of the whorl-section and tuberculation shown by typical specimens of *I. fremonti* make the characteristics of that species sufficiently broad to also encompass the specimens identified as *I. comanchensis.*"

I. fremonti is distinct from *I. varians* because of its larger size, lower stratigraphic occurrence, and whorl shape. *I. dorsetensis vectensis* Spath has more widely spaced ribs and a regular cycle of tubercle occurrence. *I. subspiniger* has better-developed lateral tubercles.

OCCURRENCE: The most abundant zone is just above the Kiamichi-Duck Creek contact although several specimens in the collections of the BEG are labeled Kiamichi. Numerous specimens are in the collections of the various universities in Texas and were obtained from central and north Texas and southern Oklahoma. Many are in the Renfro collection, U.S. National Museum.

REPOSITORY: British Museum (Natural History) 12667 (holotype); BEG 21059 (plasto-type), 20987, 35368; TCU 1145, 1146

Idiohamites varians (Scott)
(Figs. 8c, 9; Pl. 2, figs. 1–10)

Hamites varians SCOTT, 1924, Texas Christian Univ. Quart., v. 1, p. 8, 11–17, 19, Pls. 1–3, Pl. 4, figs. 1, 2, 4, 7, 9, Pl. 7, figs. 3, 4, Pl. 8, figs. 1–3, Pl. 9, figs. 1, 3–5, 7; WINTON, 1925, Univ. Texas Bull. 2544, p. 53, Pl. 6, fig. 1; SCOTT, 1926, Univ. Grenoble Thèse, Faculty Sci., p. 62, 65; ADKINS, 1928, Univ. Texas Bull. 2838, p. 19, 208, 210, Pl. 12, fig. 5; SPATH, 1939, Palaeont. Soc. London Mon., pt. 13, p. 598

Hamites polyseptus SCOTT, 1924, Texas Christian Univ. Quart., v. 1, p. 13, 17–18, Pl. 4, figs. 3, 4, 5, 8, Pl. 9, fig. 2; SCOTT, 1926, Univ. Grenoble Thèse, Faculty Sci., p. 62, 65; ADKINS, 1928, Univ. Texas Bull. 2838, p. 19, 208, 210

Idiohamites varians PERKINS, 1961, Geol. Soc. America Mem. 83, p. 27; SWENSEN, 1963, Brigham Young Univ. Geol. Studies, v. 9, pt. 2, p. 74–75, Pl. 2, figs. 1–10

A highly variable series of small heteromorphs is included under the name *I. varians.*

"Scott (1924) stated that he expected to be able to differentiate several species and possibly genera from this group. His efforts, as well as those of the present writer, have merely demonstrated that there are gradational forms between each distinct type, and that a further division of this species is impractical." (Swensen, 1963, p. 74)

Small-sized, straight and curved specimens known; ribs low, simple, continuous over venter, absent on dorsum. Compressed whorl section (Fig. 8c); small tubercles of variable occurrence, commonly on every second or third rib but tuberculation may change several times on one specimen, much variation on different specimens. Young stages nontuberculate; tubercles may appear when individual 1–2.5 mm diameter. Specimen may become non-tuberculate at later stage after having tubercles. Tubercles alternate in position on different sides of specimen in some individuals; one specimen has two ribs jointed at single tubercle.

REMARKS: Swensen (1963) studied all variations of this species in an attempt to determine the existence of more than a single type. He determined that many combinations of tubercles and ribs can occur on a single individual, including two tubercles per rib on every rib to as many as six nontuberculate ribs between tuberculate ribs and even one tubercle on every other rib. Some of these variations are figured on Plate 2.

Hamites polyseptus Scott, 1924, was considered a junior synonym of *I. varians* by Swensen (1963) because the wide range of characteristics included in *I. varians* easily encompassed *H. polyseptus*. Scott (1924) considered *H. polyseptus* distinct from *I. varians* because of the close spacing of the sutures. However, as Swensen (1963) has pointed out, the spacing of chambers is probably controlled by environmental conditions. All other characteristics of *H. polyseptus* are the same as *I. varians*. Sutures at two stages are illustrated (Fig. 9).

Figure 9. *Suture of* Idiohamites varians (2 mm, 4.6 mm; ×4.5)

I. varians is not closely related to any other species known to the writer.

OCCURRENCE: The holotype and many specimens labeled *H. polyseptus* by Scott were collected from the upper part of the Duck Creek Formation northeast of Denison, Texas.

REPOSITORY: TCU 1079 (holotype), TCU 1094a, 1094b, 1098a, 1148; BEG 35369, 35370, 35371, 35372

Idiohamites n. sp.
(Fig. 10a; Pl. 2, fig. 16)

Idiohamites sp. SWENSEN, 1963, Brigham Young Univ. Geol. Studies, v. 9, pt. 2, p. 76, Pl. 2, fig. 16

Swensen (1963) figured a single specimen which is similar to *I. fremonti* but which differs because of the lateral curving of the ribs. Only two specimens have been examined by the writer and both illustrate an adapertual curving of ribs on the lateral flanks below the mid-lateral position. Tubercles very small but on every rib at ventrolateral position; compressed whorl section (Fig. 10a).

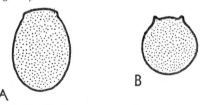

Figure 10. *Costal whorl sections, Family Anisoceratidae.* (A) *Idiohamites* n. sp. (× 1); (B) *Allocrioceras annulatum* (× 1)

OCCURRENCE: The figured specimen is from the Duck Creek Formation at Ft. Worth.
REPOSITORY: TCU 1147

Genus *Allocrioceras* Spath, 1926

Species of this genus are similar to *Idiohamites* but are more finely ribbed with fine-pointed nodes and early stages are helical. The largest specimens studied are curved fragments and no straight shaft has been found. Ribs are normally thin and high.

Swensen (1963) described a single fragment of this genus with a pear-shaped whorl section which distinguishes it from all *Allocrioceras* species. The ribbing is fine and closely spaced as in other species. The specimen was from the Tropic Shale of Utah and no equivalent Texas species is known.

Powell (1963) has described an *Allocrioceras* sp. from the Salmurian of northern Mexico, and Young (1963) has described *A. hazzardi*, a new species from the Boquillas of west Texas. This latter species may be an *Anisoceras*.

Allocrioceras annulatum (Shumard)
(Figs. 10b, 11; Pl. 5, figs. 1, 2, 10, 12)

Ancyloceras annulatus SHUMARD, 1860, Acad. Sci. St. Louis Trans., v. 1, p. 595; BOYLE, 1893, U.S. Geol. Survey Bull. 102, p. 40; SCOTT, 1926, Univ. Grenoble Thèse, Faculty Sci., p. 153; ADKINS, 1933, Univ. Texas Bull. 3232, p. 432
Ancyloceras ? *annulatus* STANTON, 1893, U.S. Geol. Survey Bull. 106, p. 48
Ancyloceras annulatum WHITE, 1883, U.S. Geol. Survey Terr. 12th Ann. Rept., 1878, pt. 1, p. 39, Pl. 28, fig. 10; BOYLE, 1893, U.S. Geol. Survey Bull. 102, p. 40; ADKINS, 1928, Univ. Texas Bull. 2838, p. 32, 216–217; ADKINS, 1933, Univ. Texas Bull. 3232, p. 433–434, 439
Helicoceras pariense MOREMAN, 1927, Jour. Paleontology, v. 1, Pl. 14, fig. 3
Allocrioceras annulatum MOREMAN, 1942, Jour. Paleontology, v. 16, p. 196, 208; SWENSEN, 1963, Brigham Young Univ. Geol. Studies, v. 9, pt. 2, p. 76–77, Pl. 3, figs. 1, 2, 10, 12
Allocrioceras n. sp. aff. *ellipticum* ADKINS, 1931, Univ. Texas Bull. 3101, p. 38, 63, Pl. 2, figs. 6, 8

Whorl section compressed in very small-sized specimens, nearly circular in larger individuals (Fig. 10b). All stages sharp ribs, equal, closely spaced, four to five in length equal to diameter. Less prominent on dorsum, inclined adapertually. Small sharp nodes on ventro-lateral margin of each rib. Tubercles first occur at diameters of 3–5 mm. Suture of small-sized individual illustrated (Fig. 11).

Figure 11. *Suture of* Allocrioceras annulatum (4.8 mm, × 4.5)

REMARKS. *A. annulatum* differs from *A. pariense* because it has sharp narrow ribs, in contrast to the rounded ribs on the latter. It has a more rounded whorl shape than *A. dentonense* and nodes on every rib of equal size which distinguish it from *A. larvatum* and *A. woodsi*.

OCCURRENCE: Shumard (1860) reported the type locality as Shawnee Creek, Grayson County, Texas. The specimens available for this study are from the Britton Member of the Eagle Ford in north Texas.

REPOSITORY: Location of holotype unknown. BEG 19820, 35367; BYU 392, 393, 394

Allocrioceras pariense (White)
(Fig. 12a; Pl. 2, figs. 12, 13)

Helicoceras pariense WHITE, 1877, U.S. Geog. and Geol. Survey W. of 100th Meridian, v. 4, p. 203, Pl. 19, figs. 2a–d; BOYLE, 1893, U.S. Geol. Survey Bull. 102, p. 146; STANTON, 1893, U.S. Geol. Survey Bull. 106, p. 35, 164–165, Pl. 35, figs. 2–4; SCOTT, 1926, Univ. Grenoble Thèse, Faculty Sci., p. 100–102, 152; MOREMAN, 1927, Jour. Paleontology, v. 1, p. 89, 91–93, 95, Pl. 13, fig. 3; ADKINS, 1931, Univ. Texas Bull. 3101, p. 39, 67–69; ADKINS, 1933, Univ. Texas Bull. 3232, p. 434; GREGORY, 1951, U.S. Geol. Survey Prof. Paper 226, p. 65
Exiteloceras pariense HYATT, 1894, Am. Philos. Soc. Proc., v. 32, p. 577; ADKINS, 1928, Univ. Texas Bull. 2838, p. 29–30, 32, 212, Pl. 26, fig. 3; GREGORY, 1950, U.S. Geol. Survey Prof. Paper 220, p. 104; GREGORY, 1951, U.S. Geol. Survey Prof. Paper 226, p. 36, 65

Allocrioceras pariense ADKINS, 1933, Univ. Texas Bull. 3232, p. 434, 437, 439; MOREMAN, 1942,
    Jour. Paleontology, v. 16, p. 193–194, 196, 208; ADKINS AND LOZO, 1951, Fondren Sci. Ser.,
    no. 4, p. 136, 156; SWENSEN, 1963, Brigham Young Univ. Geol. Studies, v. 9, pt. 2, p. 77–78,
    Pl. 2, figs. 12, 13

White (1877, p. 203–204) described the species as follows:

". . . whorls distinct, subcircular or very broadly oval in . . . section, increasing somewhat
rapidly in size; . . . annulations . . . cross the whorls obliquely . . . only slightly prominent
upon inner side of the whorls, but more prominent upon the upper and under sides; upon
the outer side of the whorl each annulation bears a pair of prominent nodes . . . The
annulations are apparently always simple, never coalescing, and never failing to completely
encircle the volution."

Swensen (1963) studied 50 specimens of *Allocrioceras* and only found two which could be
identified as *A. pariense*.

REMARKS: Moreman (1942) was the first to describe the differences in ribbing of *A.
pariense* and *A. annulatum*. He pointed out that the former had rounded ribs, the latter
fine and sharp ribs. Swensen (1963) pointed out that the rounded ribs and degree of round-
ing are transitional on some specimens and that the two "species" may well be population
variants (Fig. 12a).

A   B

Figure 12. *Costal whorl sections, Family Anisoceratidae.* (A) *Allocrioceras pariense* (× 1);
    (B) *Allocrioceras dentonense* (× 1)

OCCURRENCE: The holotype described by White (1877) was collected from the Tropic
Shale, southeast of Paria, Utah. Texas specimens are from the Britton Member of the Eagle
Ford in north and central Texas.
REPOSITORY: BEG 19821; BYU 395

Allocrioceras dentonense Moreman
(Fig. 12b; Pl. 1, figs. 7, 8; Pl. 2, fig. 3)

Allocrioceras dentonense MOREMAN, 1942, Jour. Paleontology, v. 16, p. 196, 209, Fig. 2h, Pl.
    34, fig. 4; SWENSEN, 1963, Brigham Young Univ. Geol. Studies, v. 9, pt. 2, p. 78–79, Pl. 1,
    figs. 7, 8, Pl. 3, fig. 3

Compressed whorl section (Fig. 12b); closely spaced ribs encircle shell, bear prominent
rounded tubercles on ventrolateral margins. About five ribs in length equal to diameter,
tubercles small, venter narrow.

REMARKS: *A. dentonense* is similar to *A. annulatum* and *A. pariense* but is considered
distinct because the whorl section is considerably more compressed and the ribbing is much
more closely spaced. It is rare in the Texas Cretaceous and in the Utah Tropic Shale, the
only areas from which it has been reported.
OCCURRENCE: Holotype was collected from the Britton Member of the Eagle Ford, east
of Lewisville, Texas.
REPOSITORY: BEG 19808; BYU 391

Allocrioceras larvatum (Conrad)

Hamites larvatus CONRAD, 1855, Phila. Acad. Nat. Sci. Proc. 7, p. 265; CONRAD, *in* EMORY,
    1857, Rept. U.S. and Mexico Boundary Survey, v. 1, pt. 2, Pl. 21, fig. 8; BOYLE, 1893, U.S.
    Geol. Survey Bull. 102, p. 144; ADKINS, 1927, Univ. Texas Bull. 2738, p. 67–68; ADKINS,
    1928, Univ. Texas Bull. 2838, p. 208–209
Allocrioceras larvatum ADKINS, 1933, Univ. Texas Bull. 3232, p. 439; MOREMAN, 1942, Jour.
    Paleontology, v. 16, p. 196, 208–209, Fig. 2; SWENSEN, 1963, Brigham Young Univ. Geol.
    Studies, v. 9, pt. 2, p. 80

Moreman (1942, p. 209) described the species as follows:

"Specimen consists of a cast of only a portion of the living chamber. Cross section of whorl ovate, only slightly higher than wide; ribs directed obliquely backward, prominent on venter but low and poorly defined on dorsum, alternate ribs have prominent ventrolateral tubercles which cause the rib to be flat across the venter, other ribs devoid of tubercles and rounded across venter. Suture not preserved."

REMARKS: This unique specimen is the only known representative of the species. The alternating tuberculate ribs distinguish it from other species of *Allocrioceras*.

OCCURRENCE: Britton Member of the Eagle Ford, Dallas County, Texas.

REPOSITORY: Academy of Natural Sciences of Philadelphia, no. 4790

Allocrioceras ? rotundatum (Conrad)

Hamites rotundatus CONRAD, 1855, Phila. Acad. Nat. Sci. Proc. 7, p. 266; BOYLE, 1893, U.S. Geol. Survey Bull. 102, p. 144; ADKINS, 1928, Univ. Texas Bull. 2838, p. 209

Allocrioceras rotundatum ADKINS, 1933, Univ. Texas Bull. 3232, p. 439

Allocrioceras ? rotundatum MOREMAN, 1942, Jour. Paleontology, v. 16, p. 196, 209; SWENSEN, 1963, Brigham Young Univ. Geol. Studies, v. 9, pt. 2, p. 80

Conrad (1855, p. 266) did not figure this species and his description is incomplete:

"Rounded ribs, distant, acute, the intervening spaces regularly and profoundly concave; back flattened with the ribs obsolete and three indistinct longitudinal lines. A cast."

This species has been referred to *Allocrioceras*, but its precise age and present locality are unknown. It was collected from Dallas County.

Family PHLYCTICRIOCERATIDAE Spath, 1926

This poorly understood family is characterized by an open plane spiral, strong ribs which normally bear ventrolateral tubercles plus a median-ventral row or a strong keel, and an oval whorl shape. The three-tubercle ornamentation is the most distinguishing feature of *Phlycticrioceras*, the type of the family, which occurs in the Texas Upper Cretaceous (Clark, 1963).

As defined by Arkell and others (1957, p. L220), this family contains only two species of two genera, both from the Upper Cretaceous (Coniacian). A new genus for a single species from the Upper Albian of Texas is here proposed for this family.

Genus *Prophlycticrioceras* n. gen.

This name is proposed for an Upper Albian species previously referred to *Hamites tanima* Adkins and Winton. The genus is characterized by slightly curved shafts, the only portion known, which bear strong ribs. The ribs have prominent ventrolateral tubercles and a median-ventral row of tubercles or a strong ventral keel. The whorl section is oval to laterally compressed.

The type species (= *Hamites tanima* Adkins and Winton) differs from *Phlycticrioceras* by its more oval whorl shape and fine intermediate ribs. Its age (Late Albian) indicates that it could well be the ancestral form, although Cenomanian and Turonian species have not yet been reported.

Prophlycticrioceras tanimum (Adkins and Winton)
(Figs. 13, 14; Pl. 24, figs. 1–7)

Hamites tanima ADKINS AND WINTON, 1920, Univ. Texas Bull. 1945, p. 20, 41–42, Fig. 4, Pl. 6, figs. 1, 2; SCOTT, 1926, Univ. Grenoble Thèse, Faculty Sci., p. 65; ADKINS, 1928, Univ. Texas Bull. 2838, p. 19, 209–210; SPATH, 1939, Palaeont. Soc. London Mon., pt. 13, p. 543

Slightly curved shaft, hexagonal (Fig. 13) to laterally compressed whorl section; heavy broad ribs on venter and lateral sides, become finer over dorsum. Finer intermediate ribs close to primary ribs, unevenly spaced; primary ribs bear prominent ventrolateral tubercles and either median ventral row tubercles or strongly arched ventral keel. Three primary ribs in length equal to diameter, may cross shell obliquely, as in type species, or straight across.

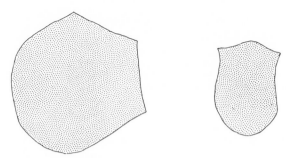

Figure 13. *Costal whorl section of* Prophlycticrioceras tanimum *n. gen. at two stages in ontogeny* (venter at top, × 3.5)

REMARKS: The venter on the type species actually falls on the inner of the "ventrolateral" tubercles, indicating that the shell may have been helically coiled. On other specimens assigned to this species which are about the same size, the venter is in the mid-ventral position. On these specimens the whorl shape is more laterally compressed and additional material may indicate that a distinct species for these forms is justified.

The primary ribs of *P. tanimum* are compounded by their association with finer intermediate ribs. Adkins and Winton (1920, p. 42) mentioned that:

". . . on the sides the primaries are conspicuously elevated, unbranched, round-topped and decrease in elevation to the dorsum, which they cross as fine continuous elevations. The auxiliary ribs (intermediates) lie on the hind slope of the primaries and are separated from them by a shallow, evenly rounded valley which, however, is bridged by an elevation running backwards from each tubercle of the primary rib to the crest of the auxiliary rib."

Four specimens of this ancestral *Phlycticrioceras* were available for this study. Suture is illustrated (Fig. 14).

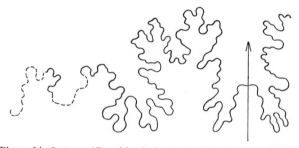

Figure 14. *Suture of* Prophlycticrioceras tanimum *n. gen.* (× 2.5)

OCCURRENCE: The type species was collected from the military road cut, half a mile north of the Texas Christian University campus, Ft. Worth, Texas. Adkins and Winton (1920) mentioned that the species was obtained from 8 feet below the bottom of the mineralized ledge in the Duck Creek.

REPOSITORY: TCU 1084 (holotype and type species); BEG 35374, 35375

Family TURRILITIDAE Meek, 1876

As originally proposed by Meek, this family included a somewhat different group of genera than it does today. All species now included coil helically but not all helical forms are placed with this family. The interpretation of this family by Arkell and others (1957, p. L220) is satisfactory and those forms which are similarly coiled but of Senonian age are considered to belong with the Nostoceratidae. The definition follows:

"Helical forms, dextral or sinistral, loosely or tightly coiled, typically regular but early and late whorls somewhat unstable; apical angle more or less acute, less than 90°; in early species, siphon is in middle of exposed side but later migrates to upper margin or even to upper internal angle of whorl; ornamented with strong ribs or tubercles or both, rarely smooth. Suture asymmetrical because of the helical coiling; primitively, lobes are bifid but they are variable and tend to trifidity."

Arkell and others (1957) follow Spath (1937) in considering *Pseudhelicoceras* and *Proturrilitoides* as the ancestral stocks of the Turrilitidae. These writers have emphasized that the two genera had different ancestors. Spath (1937, p. 508) groups the two genera and their apparent descendants together in the Turrilitidae, however, ". . . not only for systematic convenience but because . . . the difference of origin may be more apparent than real." Arkell and others (1957) indicate that *Proturrilitoides* may have been derived from a helical hamitid and that *Pseudhelicoceras* may have originated through *Protanisoceras*. A subfamily division has not been attempted because of ". . . doubt concerning the stock to which certain later genera belong . . ." (Arkell and others, 1957, p. L220).

Dubourdieu (1953) apparently considers the abberant group represented by *Raynaudia,* in the Middle Albian, as a third ancestral stock for the Turrilitidae but he does not suggest a possible origin. He does illustrate quite well the evolution of the three groups through the Albian and Cenomanian, especially in regard to the position of the siphon and its adapical migration. Breistroffer's discussion (1953) of the Turrilitidae includes proposals for several new subgenera and a single new subfamily, but exact relationships for a subfamily classification are not discussed.

If the Turrilitidae represent a closely related group, the evidence for it may be in the development of the chamber or suture pattern or something else as yet poorly understood. The source for such information will apparently come from something other than ornamentation, which is presently the basis for classification. The present system places quite similarly ornamented species in different genera, *e.g., Wintonia graysonensis* and *Plesioturrilites bosquensis, Euturrilites scheuchzerianus* and *Turrilites costatus,* and there is probably closer relationship between differently ornamented species as well. The one thing upon which specialists will presently agree is the unnatural and consequently unsatisfactory classification of most groups of Mesozoic ammonoids (Ruzhencev, 1960).

The Turrilitidae are well represented in the Texas Cretaceous by eight of the 14 genera and subgenera which the family presently includes. Only *Proturrilitoides, Paraostlingoceras, Mesoturrilites,* and *Raynaudia* are not known to occur in Texas. *Turrilitoides* and *Carthaginites* have been reported but probably are not present. The 23 species here described are the most numerous of the heteromorphs which can still be collected from the Texas Cretaceous.

Genus *Turrilitoides* Spath, 1923

Turrilitoides n. sp. ADKINS, 1933, Univ. Texas Bull. 3232, p. 371
Turrilitoides sp. PERKINS, 1961, Geol. Soc. America Mem. 83, p. 28–29, Fig. 11

This is one of the two genera of Upper Albian Turrilitidae reported in Texas but which is not definitely known. Adkins (1933) recorded a specimen from the Ft. Worth but gave no description. The repository of this specimen is unknown to the writer. More recently, Perkins (1961) listed the same genus from the Ft. Worth Limestone of the Ft. Worth-Weatherford area, but the specimen could not be obtained for the present study.

The great similarity of *Mariella nobilis* (Jukes-Browne) to species of *Turrilitoides* has been discussed by Spath (1937, p. 520): ". . . it is not always possible to distinguish the present form (*Mariella nobilis*) even from examples of the untuberculate *Turrilitoides* . . ."

The fact that specimens of *Mariella nobilis* are here described from the Ft. Worth and Denton in north Texas leads to the conclusion that those specimens previously referred to as *Turrilitoides* are specimens of *M. nobilis.*

No *Turrilitoides* from the Texas Cretaceous has been substantiated.

Genus *Ostlingoceras* Hyatt, 1900

This genus was first reported from the Texas Cretaceous by Young (1958). Its most distinguishing features are a flattened whorl side and a more or less straight arrangement of ribs which bear tubercles only on the abapical ends. One to three tubercles of unequal size may be present at this position.

This genus is known from Medial Albian to Early Cenomanian, and Breistroffer (1953) proposed the subgenus *Paraostlingoceras* for weakly tuberculate forms from the Middle Albian of Europe. Three species—one new—of this genus are described. All are Early Cenomanian.

Ostlingoceras (Ostlingoceras) davisense Young
(Fig. 15; Pl. 8, figs. 1, 3)

Ostlingoceras davisense YOUNG, 1958, Jour. Paleontology, v. 32, p. 289, Pl. 39, figs. 29, 34

Known only from sinistral high-spired specimens with more or less oval whorl section; 14–16 ribs per volution about equally strong on all portions of whorl flanks, each rib bears three prominent nodes on abapical part of specimen (Fig. 15). Nodes vary in position from

aperture

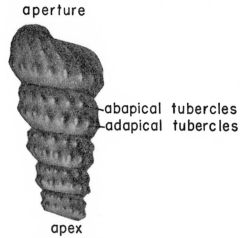

abapical tubercles
adapical tubercles

apex

Figure 15. *Terminology applied to helical heteromorphs in this report*

adoral of mid-flank for adapical row to position grouped at abapical rim of individuals, about equal distances apart, range from large to small. No suture observed.

REMARKS: This species is similar to *O. puzosiforme* Spath, particularly in the location of the nodes just abapical of the mid-point of the whorl flank and the flexious ribs. *O. davisense* can be distinguished because the flexious ribs are about half as numerous per whorl as those of *O. puzosiforme*. In addition, the nodes of the Texas species are larger than those of the European species. These same characters serve to distinguish this species from all known species.

Young (1958) expressed some question as to his generic assignment of *O. davisense* and *O. brandi*. He considered that the two species should be put with *Ostlingoceras* because of the ornamentation similarities, an assignment which seems valid.

OCCURRENCE: Base of Boquillas Formation, northeast flank of Davis Mountains, Jeff Davis County, Texas. Additional collecting by the writer at this locality did not reveal other specimens and only the few mentioned by Young (1958) were available for this study. Young did an interesting detective job in determining that the west Texas *Ostlingoceras* are reworked Early Cenomanian fossils in Late Cenomanian rock.

REPOSITORY: UT 10286 (holotype), 10782, 10280, 10287

Ostlingoceras (Ostlingoceras) brandi Young
(Pl. 8, figs. 2, 7)

Ostlingoceras brandi YOUNG, 1958, Jour. Paleontology, v. 32, p. 287–289, Fig. 1h, Pl. 40, figs. 4, 5, 7

The ornamentation of this species consists of ". . . low ribs, about 20 per whorl, some of which appear to bear incipient papillae" (Young, 1958, p. 287). Ribs moderately broad, separated from each other by distance about equal their width. Ribs equal size from venter to dorsum; weak row of nodes on adapical part. All known specimens sinistral; flanks flattened.

REMARKS: *O. brandi* is distinguished from *O. davisense*, with which it occurs in west Texas, by the number of ribs per volution and the presence of a single row of nodes. These same features also distinguish it from *O. conlini* n. sp., the only other known Texas species.

OCCURRENCE: Base of Boquillas Formation, northeastern flank of Davis Mountains, Jeff Davis County, Texas. Young (1958) indicates that this species is Early Cenomanian but redeposited in Late Cenomanian rocks.

REPOSITORY: UT 10281 (holotype), 10287, 10284, 10288, 10738, 10782E

Ostlingoceras (Ostlingoceras) conlini n. sp.
(Pl. 8, fig. 4; Pl. 9, figs. 2, 6)

This species is based on two specimens, both incomplete. Holotype is one whorl, sinistral, ribs slightly oblique, bearing single large tubercle on abapical part. Twenty-five tubercle-bearing ribs on single volution of holotype. One intermediate nontuberculate rib between primaries; intermediates project abapically to mid-flank of whorl but do not reach abapical umbilical margin. Adapically they project around umbilical wall internally. Tubercle-bearing ribs continuous around whorl. Whorl section angular.

On paratype numerous fine ribs on umbilical wall, coalesce with heavy tuberculate ribs. Intermediate nontuberculate ribs not strong on this specimen.

REMARKS: This species is distinguished from all others by the presence of a single large tubercle on the abapical portion of the large primary ribs and by the presence of at least one intermediate nontuberculate rib which extends from the adapical umbilical margin to the mid-point of the whorl flank. At maturity this intermediate rib is less apparent.

OCCURRENCE: Holotype from Conlin locality, T–51–Kms, north bank of road-cut on Seminary Drive, approximately 250 yards east of Sycamore Creek, south Ft. Worth, Tarrant County, Texas. Paratype from east and northeast of bridge over headwaters of Sycamore Creek, approximately 2.9 miles north of Crowley, on FM 731, Tarrant County, Texas. Both specimens from the Mainstreet Formation, holotype from 18–20 inches above the Pawpaw-Mainstreet contact and paratype from 8 feet above the Pawpaw-Mainstreet contact. Early Cenomanian.

REPOSITORY: Conlin 7326 (holotype), 7327

Genus *Pseudhelicoceras* Spath, 1921

This genus was proposed for certain species assigned to *Turrilites* by d'Orbigny. The earliest representatives occur in the middle-Lower Gault beds of Medial Albian age, and Dubourdieu (1953) has indicated that this genus gave rise to all of the important Upper Albian and Cenomanian Turrilitidae, *e.g.*, *Mariella*, *Hypoturrilites*, and *Ostlingoceras*. The last typical *Pseudhelicoceras* to appear is the lower middle Upper Albian *P. robertianum* which occurs in the *auritus* age beds of the Gault in England. This same species occurs in the same-age rock in Texas but, in addition, there is a peculiar form in the Texas Cretaceous which is here assigned to *Pseudhelicoceras* and occurs in younger strata than *P. robertianum*. This species occurs in the Upper Albian Pawpaw of north Texas and is morphologically transitional between *Pseudhelicoceras* and *Mariella*. Its occurrence may confirm the ancestor-descendant relationship between the two genera. It has only two tubercles on each rib and its siphon is midway between the mid-flank of the whorl and the next adapical whorl junction. Dubourdieu (1953) and Arkell and others (1957, p. L222) have pointed out that in typical *Pseudhelicoceras,* the siphon is about at the mid-flank position of the whorl. It occurs more adapical in *Mariella.* The Texas species is intermediate morphologically and stratigraphically between *Pseudhelicoceras s. s.* of the lower-middle and middle-Upper Albian and *Mariella* of the Upper Albian. It occurs too late to be the ancestral form of *Mariella* as this genus occurs in the same beds.

Except for this transitional species, all known Texas species of *Pseudhelicoceras* occur in the Ft. Worth Formation in north Texas.

The genus is distinct from all Turrilitidae because of its siphuncle position and tuberculated ribbing. Tightly coiled forms on which the siphuncle is not preserved are difficult to distinguish from *Mariella* in the Upper Albian. Four species are here described, the first report of this genus in the Texas Cretaceous. California species of *Pseudhelicoceras* have been reported recently (Matsumoto, 1959, pt. 2, p. 156; Murphy and Rodda, 1960, p. 847).

Pseudhelicoceras robertianum (d'Orbigny)
(Pl. 9, figs. 4, 5; Pl. 10, figs. 1, 5)

Turrilites robertianus D'ORBIGNY, 1842, Paris, A. Bertrand, V. Masson, v. 1, p. 585, Pl. CXLII, figs. 1–4
Pseudhelicoceras robertianum SPATH, 1922, Royal Soc. Edinburgh Trans., v. 53, pt. 1, no. 6, p. 112

This well-known species was described from the French Cretaceous 120 years ago and has since been reported from many parts of Europe and Madagascar. A rather complete synonymy is recorded in Spath (1937, p. 532).

Large, loosely coiled; large tubercles on moderately thick ribs, separated from each other by one or two nontuberculate rounded ribs which may be as large as tubercle-bearing ribs. Tubercles in four rows, large, blunt. On some specimens, fourth row hidden by umbilical debris. All ribs continuous around umbilical wall, only slightly weakened in this position. Whorl section rounded to angular.

Best-preserved Texas specimen consists of three whorls (Pl. 10, fig. 1), all of which may be body chamber. Spacing between whorls remains constant (1 cm) until final portion where it deviates to 1.5 cm. Specimen dextral, 16–20 tubercle-bearing ribs per whorl. Three rows tubercles exposed on whorl flanks, one on umbilical margin. Final whorl, tubercles larger, more pointed, no intermediate nontuberculate ribs.

REMARKS: Referred with some question to this species are two specimens (Pl. 8, fig. 8; Pl. 9, fig. 4) which have only three rows of tubercles but which agree with *P. robertianum* in other characters. On the latter, the tubercles are very long and spinose.

P. robertianum is widely distributed in Europe, and Collignon (1932) has reported it from the Upper Albian of Madagascar. All of the Texas specimens are from the Ft. Worth Limestone which is considered equivalent to the *auritus-aequatorialis* subzones of the Gault.

OCCURRENCE: This species has been found 7–15 feet below the top of the Ft. Worth in Rock Creek, south of the Johnson-Tarrant County line, and in the bed of Rock Creek, 2.5 miles south of Blum, Hill County, Texas. Specimens in the UT collections are labeled "Georgetown" (probably Ft. Worth).

REPOSITORY: Conlin 5342, 7366; UT 1623, 1624

Pseudhelicoceras breistrofferi n. sp.
(Pl. 11, figs. 1, 7)

Tightly coiled helical shell; very slightly oblique simple heavy ribs; each rib bears two long pointed tubercles, one at point of greatest convexity of shell, about mid-point of whorl flank, other at contact of next whorl abapically. Abapical tubercles visible at contact of next whorl, best observed on last whorl. Apical angle, 40°; 26 ribs on largest whorl, each bearing the two rows of tubercles. Fewer ribs on early part of shell; siphon located midway between center row of tubercles and contact with adapical whorl. Six whorls on sinistral holotype.

REMARKS: This unusual Pawpaw species illustrates a number of characteristics present on other species, but never in this unique combination. It has simple undivided ribs, with no intermediate nontuberculate ribs as in *P. elegans* (d'Orbigny), but unlike this species there are only two tubercles. This two-tubercle condition is similar to *P. subcatenatum* Spath, *P. bituberculatum* (d'Orbigny), and *P. catenatum* (d'Orbigny), but all these species have complex ribbing, *i.e.*, duplication, intermediates, *etc.* The two rows of long pointed tubercles, present on all ribs, distinguishes this species from all known *Pseudhelicoceras*.

Breistroffer (1953) and Dubourdieu (1953) have discussed the migration of the siphon during the Albian; Lower and Middle Albian forms have an abapically or medially located siphon (*Subhelicoceras* of Breistroffer), *Pseudhelicoceras s. s.* has a medially located siphuncle, and Breistroffer's *Parahelicoceras* of the lower-Upper Albian has the siphon adapical of the mid-flank.

Only a single specimen, the holotype, is known to the writer. The specimen is well preserved and larger than most of the *Mariella worthensis* specimens with which it occurs.

OCCURRENCE: From the Pawpaw Formation (uppermost Albian), 5 miles south of Ft. Worth, Tarrant County, Texas. This specimen was collected by "Nelson."

REPOSITORY: TCU 1132

Pseudhelicoceras serocostatum n. sp.
(Pl. 9, figs. 1, 3; Pl. 24, fig. 8)

Tight to moderately-loosely coiled helical shell, rounded whorl shape, deep junctions between four whorls. Slightly oblique ribs compound; one set of two ribs lie parallel or form loops, connecting at each tubercle in four-row series. Tubercles small, those of abapical row smallest. Four rows of tubercles evenly spaced, double ribs or loops between tubercles of each row closely to widely spaced. Fourth or abapical row of tubercles not visible on whorl flank but seen on abapical-most whorl on umbilical shoulder; 22–28 looped rib sets per whorl. One to three intermediate ribs may be present on latter whorls, very fine, irregularly spaced between primary looped ribs. Holotype has maximum height 5.2 cm, consists of parts of four whorls. Maximum width 4.2 cm, maximum diameter 1.8 cm. Whorl height increases from .7 cm to 1.8 cm in four whorls.

REMARKS: *P. serocostatum* n. sp., is distinguished from all known species by the rib sets or looping of ribs between the four rows of tubercles. This feature is similar to some species of *Anisoceras*. On the holotype no intermediate ribs were observed, but on one paratype one to three fine intermediates are present on the last whorl.

The two ribs between the tubercles of the four rows may be closely spaced or flare outward and merge again at the next tubercle. This looping is not prominent on the early whorls and configuration changes from tubercle to tubercle. A trace of about one fifth a complete suture can be seen on the holotype.

OCCURRENCE: Three specimens of this species are known. The holotype, Conlin 5384, and one paratype, Conlin 5445, are from the Ft. Worth Formation about 5 feet below the Ft. Worth-Denton contact, on a small tributary to Rock (Turkey) Creek, just south of the Tarrant-Johnson County line, Johnson County, Texas (Conlin loc. Jo–3–Kfw). The holotype was obtained from a nodular limestone lenticle in a shale about 7–8 inches below the paratype. Another paratype, USNM 131911, was collected by Ralph Imlay from the Rock Creek crossing, southwest of Worth Cotton Mill in Ft. Worth, in 1940. This was also in the Ft. Worth Formation.

REPOSITORY: Conlin 5384 (holotype); 5445 (paratype); USNM 131911 (paratype)

Pseudhelicoceras spp.

In the collections of the Department of Geology of the University of Texas, there are two fragmentary forms which cannot be assigned to a species with any degree of certainty because of their poor state of preservation. The whorl shape, coarse ribs, and tuberculation seem to indicate affinities with this genus. One of the specimens is from the same locality as other *P. robertianum* specimens and may be this same species. On both specimens, the ribbing is heavy and three to four small and apparently pointed tubercles can be identified on alternating ribs.

OCCURRENCE: The specimens are labeled Ft. Worth and "Georgetown," the first from Hucks Slough, Austin, Travis County, and the second from 1 mile east of Georgetown, Smiths Branch, Williamson County.

REPOSITORY: UT 770, 884

Genus *Mariella* Nowak, 1916

This genus was proposed by Nowak (1916) for a group of *Turrilites s. l.*, characterized by *T. bergeri* Brongniart. Breistroffer (1947, p. 80) proposed that *Mariella* was invalidated by *Mariaella* Gray, 1855, because of "même étymologie." He proposed *Paraturrilites* to replace this. Arkell and others (1957) pointed out that *Mariaella* does not invalidate *Mariella* (Recommendations of the Rules of Zoological Nomenclature, art. 36), and this view is here followed.

The definition of *Mariella* (Arkell and others, 1957, p. L222) follows:

"Apical angle variable; closely coiled; ribs slightly oblique, rather feeble, each with (three to) four more or less equal tubercles."

The subgenus (Mariella) is restricted to the Upper Albian, and in the Mexico-Texas Cretaceous this form is represented by five species. Two subgenera have been recognized (*Mariella* and *Plesioturrilites*), and it is here proposed to include *Wintonia* as a third subgenus.

Mariella (Mariella) nobilis (Jukes-Browne)
(Pl. 10, figs. 2–4; Pl. 11, figs. 4, 5)

Turrilites nobilis JUKES-BROWNE, 1877, Geol. Soc. London Quart., v. 33, p. 493, Pl. 21, fig. 1; SPATH, 1926, Geol. Assoc. London, Proc., v. 37, p. 429
Paraturrilites nobilis BREISTROFFER, 1947, Travaux Lab. Géol. Grenoble, t. 26, p. 65, 96; BREISTROFFER, 1953, Comptes Rendus Acad. Sci. France, t. 237, p. 1350
Mariella nobilis SPATH, 1937, Palaeont. Soc. London Mon., pt. 12, p. 520–522, Fig. 182a–c, Pl. LVIII, figs. 10, 11; BREISTROFFER, 1940, Travaux Lab. Géol. Grenoble, t. 22, p. 84, 147–148

Medium-sized shells, numerous ribs slightly oblique, each of which bears three very small nodes at abapical, central, and just below adapical junction with previous whorl. Ribs high as distance between each other, no nontuberculate intermediate ribs. Nodes very small, can be detected in places best by touch. Ribs weak on umbilical wall and, as Spath has pointed out (1937, p. 520):

"On account of the (occasionally very conspicuous) concavity of the upper surface of the whorls with the ribs produced to umbilicus, there may appear to be a fourth row of tubercles at the crenulate edge, but in most examples the ribs pass over the top without even the semblance of tuberculation."

About 28–30 ribs per whorl are present on two specimens from the Ft. Worth Formation; each consists of parts of two whorls.

REMARKS: One specimen from the Ft. Worth Formation (Conlin, 5444) has one intermediate nontuberculate rib near the abapical end of the shell. Because all other ribs bear very faint nodes, this single rib, developed on the mid-flank of the whorl only, is considered to represent some deformity due to injury or perhaps a maturity modification.

In the collections of the BEG is a single specimen consisting of about half a whorl which can be identified with *M. (M.) nobilis*. The specimen is dextral, the whorl shape rounded, and there are parts of 11 ribs exposed on what is slightly less than half a whorl. This compares favorably with the number of ribs in other representatives of this species. The ribs are slightly oblique and broader than the Ft. Worth specimens, but each rib bears three tubercles equally spaced and a little stronger than those of the Ft. Worth specimens.

Spath (1937) discussed the great similarity of this species to *Turrilitoides*. The very prominent ribs and extremely weak tubercles of *M. nobilis* make weathered specimens difficult to distinguish. Spath further pointed out that *M. nobilis* is transitional to *Turrilitoides* (p. 510). As indicated under remarks concerning *Turrilitoides*, this great similarity is probably the cause of some of the previous identifications of *Turrilitoides* in the Texas Cretaceous (Adkins, 1933; Perkins, 1961). The presence of tubercles, even though they are extremely faint, seems to be the chief distinguishing characteristic between the two.

OCCURRENCE: Conlin 7362 (loc. Hi–2–Kfw) from 3 feet, 2 inches below Ft. Worth-Denton contact, from lower part of an 18-inch shale unit below second limestone ledge below Denton contact, from banks of Rock Creek, 2.5 miles south-southeast of Blum, Hill County, Texas. Conlin 5444 from 3 feet below top of Ft. Worth Formation, 1 mile northwest of Rio Vista, Johnson County. BEG 35311 from the Denton Formation, but no other locality data can be found. This specimen was labeled by Adkins and there is little question as to his knowledge of Texas Cretaceous stratigraphy, even though Laughbaum (1960) collected intensely from the Denton in the Ft. Worth, north Texas area and did not find any heteromorphs. The general absence of ammonoids in the Denton has been noted (Adkins, 1928; Perkins, 1961), and this single specimen is unique.

This Texas occurrence is considered to come from *auritus-aequatorialis* equivalent strata.

REPOSITORY: Conlin 7362, 5444; BEG 35311

Mariella (Mariella) worthensis (Adkins and Winton)
(Fig. 16; Pl. 11, figs. 3, 6; Pl. 12, figs. 1–9; Pl. 16, figs. 4, 5)

Turrilites sp. WINTON AND ADKINS, 1920, Univ. Texas Bull. 1931, p. 69; ADKINS, 1920, Univ. Texas Bull. 1856, p. 78, Pl. 3, figs. 2, 4; ADKINS AND WINTON, 1920, Univ. Texas Bull. 1945, Pl. 7, figs. 9, 12

Turrilites worthensis ADKINS AND WINTON, 1920, Univ. Texas Bull. 1945, p. 28, 44–45, Pl. 7, figs. 10, 11, 13; ADKINS, 1920, Univ. Texas Bull. 1856, p. 78, Pl. 3, figs. 1, 6; WINTON, 1925, Univ. Texas Bull. 2544, p. 59, Pl. 6, fig. 4; BÖSE, 1928, Univ. Texas Bull. 2748, p. 146–147; ADKINS, 1928, Univ. Texas Bull. 2838, p. 24, 215, Pl. 21, fig. 1; SPATH, 1937, Palaeont. Soc. London Mon., pt. 12, p. 514, 520

Turrilites sp. B, ADKINS AND WINTON, 1920, Univ. Texas Bull. 1945, p. 45, Pl. 7, figs. 7, 8

Turrilites circumtaeniatus SCOTT, 1926, Univ. Grenoble Thèse, Faculty Sci., p. 79, 145–147, Pl. 1, figs. 10′, 10″, 11

Paraturrilites worthensis BREISTROFFER, 1947, Travaux Lab. Géol. Grenoble, t. 26, p. 66; DUBOURDIEU, 1953, Algeria, Serv. Carte Géologie Bull. 1st ser., no. 16, p. 47

Turrilites bergeri SCOTT, 1926, Univ. Grenoble Thèse, Faculty Sci., p. 144–145

"*Turrilites*" *worthensis* PERKINS, 1961, Geol. Soc. America Mem. 83, p. 39

Large apical angle (40°–50°), closely coiled, dextral and sinistral specimens in equal number. Four rows tubercles throughout on weak ribs. Rows change from strongly oblique in juvenile stages to almost straight at maturity. Ontogeny follows pattern; earliest whorls smooth, acquire weak oblique ribs with small tubercles, acquire straight ribs with larger tubercles. Abapical row of tubercles smallest. Ribbing continuous over umbilical wall and only slightly weakened. Tubercles equally spaced normally, although middle two rows slightly closer together occasionally. Siphon located adapically of the adapical-most row of tubercles, almost at junction of outer whorl rim. There are 14–18 ribs per volution; eight complete whorls noted on well-preserved specimens. Inverse relationship between size of shell and number of ribs. Small early stages may have 28 ribs per whorl whereas larger whorls often have 14–16. Ontogeny of suture illustrated (Fig. 16).

REMARKS: This species is one of the more numerous in the Texas Cretaceous and more than 1300 specimens were examined for this study. Most of these are small pyritized forms, but several large forms approaching 10 cm in height have been studied. About 60 per cent of the specimens studied are less than 3 cm in length.

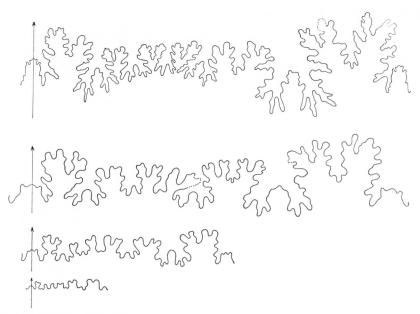

Figure 16. *Sutures of* Mariella (Mariella) worthensis (1, 3, 5, 13 mm; × 4.5, except 13-mm suture which is × 2.3)

Paedomorphosis and acceleration in the evolution of this species have been summarized here and details have recently been presented (Clark, 1962).

Scott (1926, p. 144–145) and Böse (1928, p. 146–147) considered this species to belong with various European species, and Spath indicated (1937) that he considered *M. worthensis* to be quite similar to *M. bergeri*. It is distinct from this species because of its large apical angle, ontogenetic changes, and number of ribs per whorl.

OCCURRENCE: In the collections available for this study are three boxes containing 15 specimens labeled Duck Creek and Denton. The Duck Creek specimens cannot be distinguished from the Pawpaw specimens, and the old labels do not give sufficient locality data to determine the validity of the horizon. They are probably mislabeled and belong with the more than 1300 specimens from the Pawpaw collected in north Texas.

One of the best of many localities is Sycamore Creek south of the railroad bridge, Tarrant County.

These rocks are considered to be same age as the Late Albian *dispar-perinflatum* subzones of the Gault.

REPOSITORY: BEG 21146 (holotype); numerous collections in BEG, TCU, and USNM

Mariella (Mariella) wysogorskii (Lasswitz)
(Pl. 11, fig. 2)

Turrilites wysogorskii LASSWITZ, 1904, Geol. Palaeont. Abh, new series, v. 10, heft 6, p. 235, Pl. 1, fig. 5; SCOTT, 1926, Univ. Grenoble Thèse, Faculty Sci., p. 145; ADKINS, 1928, Univ. Texas Bull. 2838, p. 26, 214–215; ADKINS AND LOZO, 1951, Fondren Sci. Ser., no. 4, p. 153
Mariella wysogorskii SPATH, 1937, Palaeont. Soc. London Mon., pt. 12, p. 516

Lasswitz (1904) reported that his specimens were from "dem grauen Kalke von Austin." Adkins (1928, p. 215) reported that the specimens of Lasswitz were from the Buda Limestone of the Shoal Creek area at Austin and that the cotypes of this species were at the University of Breslau. Inquiry by the writer to Breslau (now Wroclaw, Poland) was not acknowledged and it is assumed that the cotypes were destroyed when the university was destroyed during the war. The only other specimen of the species known to the writer is from the Buda Formation in west Texas and was collected by a University of Texas graduate student in 1957. This specimen has four rows of tubercles on very faint ribs which are strongest on abapical umbilical part. Abapical two rows of tubercles only few mm apart, about half distance between adapical two rows. Equal number tubercles in each row, 24–26 tubercles in each row per whorl. Whorl shape rounded to rectangular. Other ornamentation obscured by weathering.

Because Lasswitz's work (1904) is generally unavailable, the original description is here quoted.

"Die Schale, deren unterster Umgang ca. 2 cm hoch ist, ist linksgewunden und trägt 4 Knotenreihen. Der Durchschnitt der Umgänge ist fast rechteckig und von flachen Seiten begrenzt. Auf der Unterseite eines jeden Umgangs ziehen sich Rippen von jedem Knoten der Flanke zum Nabel derart, dass sie in Sinne der Windung verzerrt erscheinen.

Die neue Art findet ihren nächsten Verwandten in *Turrilites bergeri* Brong. Der Hauptunterschied zwischen beiden besteht vor allem in der Zahl der Knoten und in ihrer Anordnung. *Turrilites bergeri* hat 24 auf undeutlichen Querrippen stehende Knoten, während die texanische Art deren 34 zeigt. Sie sind in Längsreihen angeordnet, zwischen denen eine flache Furche verläuft. Die Grösse scheint gleich zu sein, was sich allerdings bei d'Orbigny's Abbildungen in Folge des Mangels von Grössenangaben nicht mit Bestimmtheit sagen lässt. Auch der *Turrilites tuberculatus* Bosc. zeigt in der Selbständigkeit der Knotenanordnung Aehnlichkeit, aber nur in seinen Jugendwindungen."

A free translation follows: The shell is sinistral with four rows of nodes and the lower volution is 2 cm high. The average whorl section is rectangular and flat sided. On the lower side of each volution are ribs which run from each node on the flank to the umbilicus, appearing as a distorted spiral.

The new species shows close relationship to *Turrilites bergeri* Brongniart. The chief difference between the two is in the number of nodes and their arrangement. *Turrilites bergeri* Brongniart has 24 indistinct and oblique ribs with prominent nodes whereas the Texas species has 34. They are arranged in long rows and are separated by a flat groove. The size appears to be the same as those illustrated by d'Orbigny, but there is some uncertainty because there is no size data given. It should also be pointed out that *Turrilites tuberculatus* Bosc. has a similar node arrangement, but only in the early whorls.

REMARKS: This rare species was differentiated from *M. bergeri* by both Lasswitz (1904) and Spath (1937) by the possession of 34 tubercles, as compared with 24 in *M. bergeri*. Spath considered that *M. wysogorskii* ". . . may stand in the same relationship to *M. lewesensis* as *M. miliaris* does to *M. bergeri*" (1937, p. 516). Because the types appear to have been lost, the validity of *M. wysogorskii* is difficult to substantiate. Scott reported that "Nous ne pensons pas que *T. wysogorskii* doive être séparé de *bergeri*" (1926, p. 145).

OCCURRENCE: Type specimens from the Buda Limestone at Austin, Texas. Single specimen available for this study from unit 2 of the Buda Limestone, 2 miles northeast of Smokey Headquarters of the Dunagen 96 Ranch, east of Van Horn Creek, Presidio County, Texas. The specimen was collected by Mr. Phillip Braithwaite in 1957 and is Cenomanian in age.

REPOSITORY: Types either in repository at the University of Wroclaw, Poland, or lost. Presidio County specimen, UT 30537

Mariella (Mariella) camachoensis (Böse)
(Pl. 13, fig. 8; Pl. 18, fig. 8)

Turrilites camachoensis Böse, 1923, Geol. Inst. Mexico Bol., v. 42, p. 149–151, Pl. X, figs. 32–37

Paraturrilites (?) *camachoensis* Dubourdieu, 1953, Algerian Serv. Carte Géologie Bull., 1st ser., no. 16, p. 49, 55

According to Böse (1923), in the area of Camacho, Mexico, this is the most common of the species of *Mariella*. It is characterized by a fairly slender shell, shallow junction between whorls. Flanks of whorls angular, whorl section trapezoid. Ornamentation consists of three rows pointed tubercles on whorl flank, fourth row on abapical margin of umbilical margin hidden by overlap of next abapical whorl, adjacent row tubercles at junction of whorls.

Between first row tubercles and posterior part of junction of whorls is slight groove. Small ribs adapical of adapical-most row tubercles weak, do not extend far either adapically or abapically. Apical angle 35°–40°. About 19 rows tubercles per whorl.

REMARKS: Böse (1923) pointed out the similarity of this species to *Turrilites costatus* but distinguished it on the basis of number of tubercles. This species is similar to *T. costatus* of the Cenomanian and may be an ancestral type. The presence of four rows of tubercles, however, is a distinguishing feature. Of the several specimens at the Geologic Institute of Mexico, none is well preserved and all are quite small.

The specimen figured by Böse (1923, Pl. X, figs. 32, 35) and here (Pl. 18, fig. 8) is designated the lectotype.

OCCURRENCE: Vraconian (Upper Albian), between Camacho and the Trinidad mine, Zacatecas, Mexico.

REPOSITORYS IGM 1075–C (lectotype)

Mariella (Mariella) carrancoi (Böse)
(Pl. 13, figs. 1–4, 7, 10)

Turrilites carrancoi BÖSE, 1923, Geol. Inst. Mexico Bol., v. 42, p. 147–148, Pl. X, figs. 25–31; DUBOURDIEU, 1953, Algeria, Serv. Carte Géologie Bull., 1st ser., no. 16, p. 47, 49, 55
Turrilites multipunctatus BÖSE, 1923, Geol. Inst. Mexico Bol., v. 42, p. 154–155, Pl. X, figs. 48–58; DUBOURDIEU, 1953, Algeria, Serv. Carte Géologie Bull., 1st ser., no. 16, p. 50; SPATH, 1937, Palaeont. Soc. London Mon., pt. 12, p. 513

Shell slender, junction of whorls deep, flank of whorl trapezoid. Ornamentation consists of three rows tubercles on abapical portion of whorl, fourth row hidden by next abapical whorl. Adapical-most row on fairly strong projection give appearance of groove below. Each row consists of 22–34 tubercles, pointed, separated by intervals wider than width of base of tubercles. Apical angle 40°–48°.

REMARKS: *T. multipunctatus* Böse described at the same time as *T. carrancoi* (1923, p. 147–148), is considered to be a junior synonym. It appeared on later pages in Böse's original volume (1923). The principal reason for separating the two originally was evidently the number of tubercles per whorl, a characteristic not of specific value in other species of *Mariella*. As defined by Böse (1923, p. 154–155), *T. multipunctatus* has 32 tubercles per whorl and *T. carrancoi* 22–24 tubercles per whorl. This is the only difference of note, and the variation of eight to 10 tubercles is less than on other species of *Mariella* studied for this report.

Several other specimens described by Böse (1923) probably belong here, but the material is so poorly preserved that the present writer cannot put them in any species with a degree of certainty. This includes *T.* aff. *wiestii*, *Turrilites* sp., *T.* aff. *acutus*, and a second specimen referred to as *T.* aff. *acutus* by Böse.

Mariella (Mariella) carrancoi was compared with *T. gresslyi* Pictet and Campiche by Böse (1923), however; the latter has only three rows of tubercles. Dubourdieu (1953) compared *M. carrancoi* with *M. hillyi*, *M. kerkourensis*, and *T. harchaensis*. The number and spacing of tubercles and absence of ribs distinguish this species from the others.

A very interesting observation on the two Mexican species of *Mariella* is the fact that the typical *Plesioturrilites* groove seems to be anticipated with a slight projecting of the two adapical rows of tubercles. This groove appears first in the Cenomanian species of this genus (with the single exception already noted), and the Mexican species are suggestive of an ancestral type. The occurrence of an Upper Albian *Plesioturrilites* (this report) rules out the possibility that this species could be the actual ancestor.

The specimen illustrated by Böse (1923, Pl. X, figs. 27, 30) and in this report (Pl. 13, fig. 3) is designated the lectotype.

OCCURRENCE: Vraconian (Upper Albian), between the Camacho and Trinidad mine, Zacatecas, Mexico.

REPOSITORY: IGM 1076–C (lectotype)

Subgenus *Mariella (Plesioturrilites)* Breistroffer, 1953

Breistroffer (1953) proposed this subgenus for those species of *Mariella* characterized by a prominent spiral depression between the middle rows of tubercles. If the form reported by Stoliczka (1866) is not of this group (Scott, 1926, p. 83), then *Plesioturrilites* is apparently restricted to North America and is most common in the Texas Cretaceous. Arkell and others (1957, p. L222) indicate that it occurs only in Texas. However, it is now known to occur in Oklahoma, northern Mexico (Perkins, 1961), and recently Matsumoto (1959, pt. 2, p. 156) has made report of the first *Plesioturrilites* from California.

This subgenus is represented in the Texas Cretaceous by three species—one new. It is one of the more common heteromorphs which can still be collected in the famous north Texas rocks and has long been considered as an excellent index fossil to rocks of Early Cenomanian age. One Late Albian specimen is known to the writer.

Mariella (Plesioturrilites) brazoensis brazoensis (Roemer)
(Pl. 14, figs. 3–5; Pl. 16, figs. 1, 6)

Turrilites brazoensis ROEMER, 1849, Bonn, Adolph Marcus, p. 415; ROEMER, 1852, Bonn, Adolph Marcus, p. 37, Pl. 3, fig. 2; SHUMARD, 1860, Acad. Sci. St. Louis Trans., v. 1, no. 4, p. 605; HILL, 1889b, Texas Geol. Survey Bull. 4, p. 23; HILL, 1901, U.S. Geol. Survey 21st Ann. Rept., pt. 7, Pl. 37, fig. 3a; LASSWITZ, 1904, Geol. Palaeont. Abh., new ser., v. 10, heft 6, p. 233–234, Pl. 2, fig. 2; WHITNEY, 1911, Texas Acad Sci. Proc. 12, p. 24, Pl. 12, fig. 1; ADKINS AND WINTON, 1920, Univ. Texas Bull. 1945, p. 30, 45–46, Pl. 7, figs. 14, 15; WINTON AND ADKINS, 1920, Univ. Texas Bull. 1931, p. 21, 70–71; WINTON, 1925, Univ. Texas Bull. 2544, p. 31–32, 60–61, Pl. 5, fig. 6; SCOTT, 1926, Univ. Grenoble Thèse, Faculty Sci., p. 82–83, 147; ADKINS, 1927, Univ. Texas Bull. 2738, p. 55; BÖSE, 1928, Univ. Texas Bull. 2748, p. 25, 152–154, 158, 160, 166, 199–201, Pl. 1, fig. 1; ADKINS, 1928, Univ. Texas Bull. 2838, p. 17, 25, 214, Pl. 21, fig. 10; ADKINS, 1933, Univ. Texas Bull. 3232, p. 384–387; EIFLER, 1943, Geol. Soc. America Bull., v. 54, p. 1631; BAILEY, EVANS, AND ADKINS, 1945, Am. Assoc. Petroleum Geologists Bull., v. 29, p. 181; GOLDICH AND ELMS, 1949, Geol. Soc. America Bull., v. 60, p. 1140; FERAY, 1949, Shreveport Geol. Soc. 17th Ann. Field Trip Guidebook, p. 49; ADKINS AND LOZO, 1951, Fondren Sci. Ser., no. 4, p. 152–154, Pl. 1, fig. 19; STEPHENSON, 1952, U.S. Geol. Survey Prof. Paper 242, p. 8; PERKINS AND ALBRITTON, 1955, Fondren Sci. Ser., no. 5, p. 23; YOUNG, 1959, Am. Jour. Sci., v. 257, p. 760
Turrilites cf. *T. brazoensis* STEPHENSON, 1944, Am. Assoc. Petroleum Geologists Bull., v. 28, p. 1540
Paraturrilites (Plesioturrilites) brazoensis BREISTROFFER, 1953, Comptes Rendus Acad. Sci. France, t. 237, p. 1351
Plesioturrilites brazoensis YOUNG, 1959, Am. Jour. Sci., v. 257, p. 758, 761
Mariella (Plesioturrilites) brazoensis ARKELL, KUMMEL, AND WRIGHT, *in* MOORE, 1957, Treatise on Invertebrate Paleontology: Geol. Soc. America and Univ. Kansas Press, pt. L, p. L222, Fig. 249; PERKINS, 1961, Geol. Soc. America Mem. 83, p. 40, 42, 90–91, Pl. 32, fig. 2, Pl. 33, figs. 4, 5

Large helical shell, up to 8 inches in diameter and 1 foot in length. Helically coiled, tight, overlap of whorls. Four rows bullate tubercles in two sets on whorl flanks. Abapical set usually smaller, separated from adapical set by spiral groove usually as deep as bounding tubercles are high. Abapical tubercles are not so widely spaced as larger adapical tubercles. All four rows aligned obliquely on whorl flank, rounded to bullate, equal number in each row. Apical angle 40°–45°, complete specimens rare. Suture rarely preserved (Adkins and Winton, 1920, Pl. 7, fig. 15).

REMARKS: This species is one of the best known and widespread of the Texas Turrilitidae. South of Ft. Worth, the thin beds of the Mainstreet have yielded hundreds of specimens. For more than 40 years this species has been used as a zonal fossil in the "Washita" of north Texas (Adkins and Winton, 1920, p. 30).

The early reports of this species listed five rows of tubercles (Roemer, 1852; Hill, 1901; Adkins and Winton, 1920), the fifth row occurring near the abapical umbilical border. Adkins (1928) corrected these earlier reports. Occasionally on very large-sized specimens, the later whorls have indications of an additional row caused by swelling of the ribs, as they are folded over the umbilical border, but this is rare.

OCCURRENCE: This species is common in the Mainstreet and overlying Grayson in north and south-central Texas. In 1928, Adkins noted that it had been found in the Mainstreet and Grayson but reported that it was rare or unknown in west Texas. It is now known in the basal Del Rio in the Trans-Pecos area and in the upper Espy of the Quitman Mountains in extreme western Texas. In addition, Perkins (1961) reported this species in the upper Aurora Limestone and Georgetown and Del Rio equivalents of Coahuila, Mexico. All of these rocks are considered to be Cenomanian.

One very important occurrence is the location of a single specimen in the Weno Formation in north Texas. Mr. J. P. Conlin found the specimen in south Ft. Worth, Tarrant County, on a high bluff on the east bank of Sycamore Creek. It was found in place, 10–11 feet below the Weno-Pawpaw contact, and confirmation of the stratigraphic occurrence is given by Mr. Frank Crane of Dallas, who observed the specimen in place before it was collected by Conlin. The specimen is fragmentary but shows quite well the distinguishing characteristics of *M. (Plesioturrilites) brazoensis.* This is the only specimen known from below the Mainstreet and is the oldest known *P. brazoensis.*

REPOSITORY: Paleontological Institute, University of Bonn, Roemer no. 54 (holotype): BYU 436 (plastotype); numerous specimens in all museums and university collections in Texas. Specimen figured by Adkins and Winton (1920, Pl. 7, figs. 14, 15) TCU 1089; and Adkins (1928, Pl. 21, fig. 10) BEG 21057

Mariella (Plesioturrilites) brazoensis pecosensis n. subspecies
(Pl. 15, figs. 4, 5)

This subspecies name is proposed for those specimens of *Plesioturrilites* which differ from *P. brazoensis brazoensis* principally in the possession of an unequal number of tubercles in the two double rows. They consist of four whorls which increase rapidly in size from early to late whorls; the largest is 7 cm high and 9.5 cm in diameter. The holotype of this variety has a maximum height of 16 cm. Ornamentation consists of four rows of tubercles, two rows below and two above a prominent spiral groove. The abapical two rows contain tubercles unequal in size but equal in number, and the adapical two rows consist of medium-sized bullate tubercles which are more numerous in any given whorl distance than the tubercles of the abapical two rows. On the holotype, the largest whorl has 15 tubercles in the abapical two rows and 22 in the adapical two rows. About 25 per cent more tubercles are present in the adapical rows than in the abapical rows of all specimens studied.

Abapical-most row consists of medium- to small-sized tubercles which are rounded and closely spaced. The distance between each, on the largest whorl, is not quite as great as the width of the tubercles. The abapical row bounding the groove consists of large pointed tubercles, the largest on the specimen. The groove separating the two double rows is not quite as deep as the height of the highest bounding tubercles. The whorl shape is rounded to quadrate.

REMARKS: This subspecies can be distinguished from *P. brazoensis brazoensis* by the abrupt increase in whorl size during ontogeny and by the fact that there are about 25 per cent more tubercles in the adapical two rows than in the abapical two rows. The geographic distribution of *P. brazoensis pecosensis* n. sub., is of interest as all specimens of the species found in west Texas by the writer belong to the new variety. This includes the holotype from Val Verde County and several other specimens from the Espy Formation in the southern Quitman Mountains in west Texas. In the central Texas area where *P. brazoensis brazoensis* is abundant, only very few specimens of *P. brazoensis pecosensis* n. sub. have been found. None of these vary by the 25 per cent factor in the number of tubercles as do the west Texas specimens. This may be an excellent example of evolution involving geographic separation (Clark, 1962).

OCCURRENCE: Holotype from 1 foot above the base of the Del Rio Formation, exposed in the road-cut at the U.S. 90 Pecos River Bridge, Val Verde County, Texas (BYU loc.

12012). Other specimens from the upper Espy Formation in southern Quitman Mountains, a few miles north of Texas-Mexico border.

REPOSITORY: BYU 396 (holotype)

Mariella (Plesioturrilites) rhacioformis n. sp.
(Pl. 14, figs. 1, 2; Pl. 15, figs. 2, 3; Pl. 16, figs. 2, 3)

Medium- and small small-sized specimens, holotype consists of three whorls, largest with maximum diameter of 40 mm. Maximum height of large whorl 24 mm. Whorls rounded to quadrate; ornamentation consists of two sets ribs separated by deep spiral groove. Holotype has 18 rib sets per whorl. Ribbing oblique, all known specimens sinistral. Ribs appear to consist of joined tubercles and occasionally small peaks appear on ribs at point of principal growth, most often on abapical ribs, not observed on adapical ribs.

REMARKS: This species is closely related to *P. brazoensis* from which it originated through the process of paedomorphosis (*see* discussion under evolution). Winton (1925) mentioned this type occurring with *P. brazoensis,* and in the collections of the University at Grenoble, France, there is an excellent example of *P. rhacioformis* n. sp. which was labeled *Turrilites* n. sp., probably by Gayle Scott, more than 40 years ago. This species occurs most abundantly in the middle and upper layers of the Grayson Formation which is stratigraphically younger than the greatest concentrations of *P. brazoensis*. There are complete transitions between the two species (Clark, 1962).

The specimen described by Lasswitz (1904) as *T. peramplus* may possibly be the same as *P. rhacioformis* but, because neither holotype nor any specimens of this species are available for study, no comparisons can be made.

The ribbing separated by a groove distinguishes this species from all others.

OCCURRENCE: The holotype is from the Grayson Formation, possibly of Travis County, but the exact locality data were not recorded in the Bureau of Economic Geology where the specimen is housed. Numerous individuals have been collected from the upper part of the Mainstreet and middle and upper parts of the Grayson in north Texas, especially at Grayson's Bluff, northeast of Roanoke, Denton County, Texas. The strongly ribbed "varieties" of *P. brazoensis,* found in most museums, belong to this species, although occasionally a weathered *P. brazoensis* may be confused with *P. rhacioformis* n. sp.

REPOSITORY: BEG 35313 (holotype); BYU 397, 400, 402

Mariella (Plesioturrilites) bosquensis (Adkins)
(Figs. 17, 18a; Pl. 15, fig. 1; Pl. 17, figs. 1–16; Pl. 18, figs. 6, 10)

Turrilites bosquensis ADKINS, 1920, Univ. Texas Bull. 1856, p. 57, 59, 76–78, Pl. 3, figs. 3, 7; SCOTT, 1926, Univ. Grenoble Thèse, Faculty Sci., p. 83, 86, 88, 92, 147–149, Pl. 3, figs. 5, 6; BÖSE, 1928, Univ. Texas Bull. 2748, p. 26–27, 154–157, 166, 200, 206–210, Pl. 1, figs. 8–23, Pl. 2, figs. 2, 18, Pl. 3, figs. 4–10, Pl. 4, figs. 1, 2; ADKINS, 1928, Univ. Texas Bull. 2838, p. 18, 25, 215, Pl. 23, fig. 12; ADKINS AND LOZO, 1951, Fondren Sci. Ser., no. 4, p. 154; STEPHENSON, 1952, U.S. Geol. Survey Prof. Paper 242, p. 197
Mariella (Plesioturrilites) bosquensis PERKINS, 1961, Geol. Soc. America Mem. 83, p. 41

Adkins based his study (1920) on 10 specimens collected from the middle member of the Del Rio Formation, on the east bank of the South Bosque River, west of Waco, Texas. Hundreds of specimens have been collected since 1920 and the species is now understood to include a broader range of characters.

Holotype small, 22 mm long, consists of five whorls which do not include any part of body chamber. Apical end also missing. Four rows tubercles and, as in all species of *Plesioturrilites,* spiral groove separates two double rows. Tubercles of adapical two rows larger than abapical two rows. Holotype has 11 large tubercles 2 mm apart on final whorl in adapical rows and 14 in abapical rows. Apical angle 39° average for 50 specimens measured. Siphon at adapical margin of adapical tubercles. Two sizes in suture development illustrated (Figs. 17, 18a).

Figure 17. *Suture of* Mariella (Plesioturrilites) bosquensis (1.5 mm, × 9)

Holotype differs from majority of sample studied, 18–26 tubercles per whorl, rather than 11 common, up to 30 on few specimens observed; scatter diagrams and standard deviations studied but results interpreted as indicating that all sample constitutes single species. Tubercles smaller on most specimens than on holotype.

REMARKS: Adkins' report of an unequal number of tubercles in the abapical rows (1920, p. 76) was criticized by Böse (1928, p. 206):

"He" (referring to Adkins) "also says that the tubercles on the third row (abapical) are more closely spaced and more numerous than in the two first rows (adapical). This is equally in error; the tubercles are more closely spaced because the spiral on which they stand is smaller than those of the other two rows, but the number of tubercles is the same."

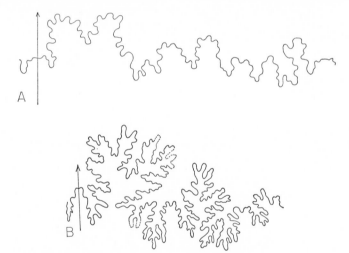

Figure 18. *Sutures of Family Turrilitidae.* (A) *Mariella (Plesioturrilites) bosquensis* (13 mm, × 3); (B) *Hypoturrilites tuberculatus,* Texas specimen (× 3)

Böse's observations were based on study of several hundred specimens from Texas and Mexico, some of which were studied during the present investigation. Although the majority of specimens of *P. bosquensis* do have equal numbers of tubercles in each row, the holotype and numerous other specimens do possess unequal numbers, as originally reported by Adkins. On most specimens there is also a small ridge which extends from the abapical row of tubercles to the umbilicus.

One interesting observation is that, in 1300 specimens examined for this study, only four coil dextrally; all others are sinistral. In a similar-size sample of *Mariella worthensis,* there was a 50–50 division into dextral and sinistral. Coiling direction is not transitional, and because a specimen coils either dextrally or sinistrally the four dextral specimens in the 1300 sample probably represent a single mutation for coiling direction in the population.

Paedomorphosis and caenogenesis with *Wintonia graysonensis* is discussed under evolution. Paedomorphosis is probably responsible for a small percentage of the variation which can be noted.

The body chamber, partially preserved, has been found on several specimens but the exact configuration is still in doubt (Pl. 17, figs. 2, 10, 14).

In summary, most specimens of this fauna are small pyritized forms, and the specimen figured by Scott (1926, Pl. 3, fig. 5) is one of the few nonpyritized forms known. The majority of the specimens studied differ from the holotype in possession of a greater number of tubercles, and evidently the holotype is truly representative of about 2 per cent of 1300 individuals studied.

OCCURRENCE: This species has been found in the Grayson and Del Rio Formations of Texas and Mexico. Holotype is from the middle member of the Del Rio, on the east bank of the South Bosque River, west of Waco, Texas. Perkins (1961) indicated that the species is no longer abundant but can still be collected from the Del Rio.

REPOSITORY: BEG 20990 (holotype)

Subgenus *Mariella* (*Wintonia*) Adkins, 1928

What Adkins called the genus *Wintonia* (1928) is here considered a subgenus of *Mariella*. This consideration is based on the very close similarity of the species assigned to *Mariella* with *Wintonia graysonensis*, the only known species. *W. graysonensis* shows greatest similarity to species of *Plesioturrilites* because they both possess the deep spiral groove separating two double rows of tubercles. It is distinguished from other subgenera because it possesses an early straight shaft which merges only in later ontogenetic stages with a normally coiled helical shell. This same feature has been the basis for separating *Wintonia* generically from others of the *Mariella* group. The study of the evolution of various species of the *Mariella* group indicates caenogenesis between *Plesioturrilites bosquensis* and *Wintonia graysonensis* (Clark, 1962). This is summarized under evolution of this report.

Spath (1942, p. 720) interpreted the early straight shaft of *Wintonia* as an unstable character and ". . . not recapitulatory and does not indicate a polyphyletic origin of the Turrilitidae." The writer agrees with Spath and considers that *Wintonia* is closely related to *Mariella* and *Plesioturrilites*. All have four rows of tubercles; *Plesioturrilites* and *Wintonia* have a spiral groove which coils around the shell and separates the two double rows of tubercles; *Wintonia* has an early straight shaft which merges during later ontogeny with a helical shell.

Mariella (*Wintonia*) *graysonensis* (Adkins)
Pl. 18, figs. 1–5, 7, 9, 11–13

Turrilites sp. (whiplash) ADKINS, 1920, Univ. Texas Bull. 1856, p. 57
Wintonia graysonensis ADKINS, 1928, Univ. Texas Bull. 2838, p. 25, 213, Pl. 23, figs. 7–9; ADKINS, 1933, Univ. Texas Bull. 3232, p. 395; SPATH, 1942, Palaeont. Soc. London Mon., pt. 16, p. 719; ARKELL, KUMMEL, AND WRIGHT, *in* MOORE, *Editor*, 1957, Treatise on Invertebrate Paleontology: Geol. Soc. America and Univ. Kansas Press, pt. L, p. L222

Adkins' original description of the species (1928, p. 213) follows:

"Limonitic micromorph; small, tall, high-spired turriliticone, ribbed and tuberculate on body portion. Initial portion (broken) consists of an extended, smooth limb, grooved on the inner side, and septate. It passes into a tight, ribbed, tuberculate spiral with prominently convex sides, deep sutures, narrow, inconspicuous ribs and on the ribs three rows of tubercles. The upper two rows of tubercles bound a projecting shelf which occupies the middle of the volution; below it is a narrow, spiral depression, beneath which at the overlap, there is a third row of somewhat smaller tubercles. Aperture unknown; broken portion suggests a typical *Turrilites*. Suture unknown."

There are 18–22 tubercles per volution on the apertural end and 21–25 on the apical end. There are four distinct rows of tubercles, not three, as indicated by Adkins.

REMARKS: Adkins (1928) indicated that only three rows of tubercles were present in this species but in all specimens available for this study there were four rows, although the abapical-most row is quite small.

The spiral groove which winds around the shell and separates the two double rows of tubercles is considered of some importance. The same type groove and tuberculation is present in all adult *Wintonia* specimens as in *Plesioturrilites bosquensis,* and those specimens which have no straight shaft preserved cannot be distinguished from *P. bosquensis.* This fact led the writer to believe that the two species could be synonyms; *i.e.,* all forms on which the straight shaft has not been preserved are called *P. bosquensis* and those forms with the shaft preserved have been called *W. graysonensis*. Later in the study, a few complete forms of *P. bosquensis* with normal helical coiling to the tip were found. This makes it necessary to emphasize the fact that only those forms which have the straight part preserved are presently regarded as *Wintonia,* and many specimens on which this shaft has been broken are presently identified as *P. bosquensis.* All characteristics of the ornamentation of the two species have been treated statistically, and none of the results have been considered significant enough for distinction. This interesting phenomenon is considered to be an example of caenogenesis in the evolution of these species (section under evolution, and Clark, 1962).

The holotype and two paratype specimens figured by Adkins (1928) were supposedly placed in the Repository of Texas Christian University but E. Heuer of that institution has reported that they have no record of the specimens. Other attempts to locate the maerial have been unsuccessful, and either the specimens are lost or have been placed in some unknown collection. Because they may be present in the unsorted collections of the late W. S. Adkins, no lectotype is designated.

This species has been found only in Texas.

OCCURRENCE: The holotype was collected from the Grayson Formation (Early Cenomanian) at Grayson Bluff, east of Roanoke, Denton County, Texas. Specimens for this study were collected at the type locality and recovered from the BEG collections labeled *P. bosquensis,* from the Del Rio and Grayson Formations in a creek about 2 miles southwest of Aquilla, Hill County, Texas.

REPOSITORY: BEG 35350, 35351, 35352, 35353, 35354, 35355, 35356, 35357

Genus *Hypoturrilites* Dubourdieu, 1953

This genus was proposed to include those species on which the ". . . ribs are almost absent and middle row of tubercles contain fewer and much larger tubercles than remainder" (Arkell and others, 1957, p. L222). Slightly more than a dozen species are presently recognized and except for two new species here described, all are best known outside of North America. Only one Texas species is conspecific with a European form.

Dubourdieu (1953, p. 43) indicated that ancestors of this genus were of the group of *Pseudhelicoceras* and may have branched off in the Late Albian from the same ancestral line as *Mariella.* Because only Early Cenomanian species of *Hypoturrilites* have been previously described, there has been a gap between supposed ancestors and the members of this genus. However, *Hypoturrilites primitivus* n. sp., from the Late Albian has characteristics which indicate that it may well be the ancestral form, as well as being the oldest described *Hypoturrilites* species.

Species of this genus are widespread in the Early Cenomanian rocks, although only three specimens representing two species have been reported from this age rock in Texas.

Hypoturrilites tuberculatus (Bosc)
(Figs. 18b, 19a, b; Pl. 19, figs. 5, 8, 9)

Turrilites roemeri WHITNEY, 1911, Texas Acad. Sci. Proc. 12, p. 24–25, Pl. 12, figs. 2, 3; ADKINS, 1928, Univ. Texas Bull. 2838, p. 26, 215; BÖSE, 1928, Univ. Texas Bull. 2748, p. 153; ADKINS AND LOZO, 1951, Fondren Sci. Ser., no. 4, p. 153

"Shell turriculate, conical, sinistral; angle (apical) 49 degrees; volutions angular in front, convex behind, overlapping; suture deep; surface ornamented with four rows of unequal tubercles; the anterior (abapical) row with about thirty-two tubercles, placed on the sutural angle at the outer end of ribs which converge toward the umbilicus; a second row of narrow more elongate tubercles is placed parallel to and behind the first row. It has the same number of tubercles as the first. Below the second, is a third row of elongate tubercles, of the same number as those in the other rows. The fourth row consists of large, rounded tubercles placed in the middle of the volution, and numbering about eleven." (Whitney, 1911, p. 25)

REMARKS: Whitney differentiated his species from *H. tuberculatus* by the spiral angle and shape of tubercles, and from *H. gravesianus* by the more clavate smaller tubercles and the fact that overlapping of adjacent whorls covers the three rows of smaller tubercles in the abapical position. This specimen has fewer tubercles than the type of *H. tuberculatus* and a greater spiral angle, but these differences can be explained by the small size of the Texas specimen and by the fact that it is slightly squashed. Actually, the specimen compares favorably with specimens of *H. tuberculatus* in many features (*e.g.*, Sharpe, 1853, Pl. 25, fig. 1). One of the most interesting comparisons (Figs. 18b, 19a, b) is the sutural similarity of the Texas specimen and *H. tuberculatus* figured by Sharpe (1853, Pl. 26, figs. 15, 16).

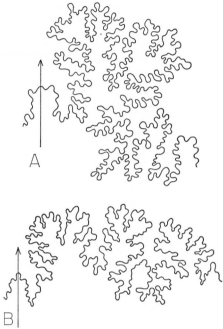

Figure 19. *Sutures of Family Turrilitidae.* (A) *Hypoturrilites tuberculatus,* English specimen, after Sharpe (1853, Pl. XXVI, fig. 16) (Magnification unknown); (B) *Hypoturrilites tuberculatus,* English specimen, after Sharpe (1853, Pl. XXVI, fig. 15) (Magnification unknown)

Sharpe (1853) was impressed by the differences of sutures of *H. tuberculatus* and *H. gravesianus* and pointed out that in specimens not well preserved the sutural differences were distinct enough for classification. In the sutures of *H. tuberculatus* available for this study the consistency in pattern is noteworthy and may indicate that sutures are of more value, in at least some Mesozoic ammonoids, than some writers have suggested (Young, 1957, p. 2).

Whitney (1911) stated that the three rows of small clavate tubercles are covered by the overlap of successive whorls. A closer examination indicates that these rows of tubercles have not been preserved on the flanks of the whorls except for the final whorl, and when their position is traced adapically from the last whorl, it becomes evident that they were not overlapped but have been removed by weathering.

OCCURRENCE: The Texas specimen was collected from the Shoal Creek (= Buda) at Austin, Texas, by F. L. Whitney. European specimens are from the Cenomanian.

REPOSITORY: UT (Whitney Collection) 10-1-592

Hypoturrilites primitivus n. sp.
(Pl. 19, figs. 1–3)

Species based on less than half of sinistral specimen which consists of body chamber and portions of final suture. Specimen small (20 mm long, 11-mm widest diameter). Ornamentation consists of row small bulate tubercles, on abapical portion of whorl, on simple oblique ribs extending toward abapical part of specimen and disappearing about one-third distance from umbilical wall. Small tubercles separated from row large tubercles at mid-whorl position by slightly concave, smooth depression. Seven large tubercles, 10 small tubercles and ribs, on fragmentary holotype. Large tubercles pointed, occupy most convex point on whorl flank. Large heavy ribs originate with these tubercles, extend adapically, disappear on umbilical wall of adapical part of whorl. At point of contact of previous whorl ribs bifurcate and pinch out; impressions of small tubercles of preceding whorl quite deep (Pl. 19, fig. 1). Whorl shape angular, siphon not quite at angle of whorl flank and umbilical slope but closer to large tubercles.

REMARKS: This species is similar to *H. carcitanensis* Matheron on which the two to three rows of small tubercles may coalesce at maturity into a single row. This latter species lacks the strong ribbing extending abapically, as is present in *H. primitivus* n. sp., and, in addition, there is no indication that the single row of small tubercles has resulted from fuson of two or three rows as is apparent in *H. carcitanensis*.

This is one of the very different Turrilitidae in the Texas Cretaceous and is not closely similar to any specimen known to the writer. The fact that there are a row of large-sized tubercles about mid-whorl in position and a row of small-sized tubercles of greater number in the abapical position confirms affinities with *Hypoturrilites*. However, the odd combination of two rows of tubercles indicates differences not previously included in this genus. In addition, the genus has been previously described only from the Cenomanian, whereas *H. primitivus* n. sp. is from the Late Albian Pawpaw Formation. It occurs with a great number of typical Pawpaw *Mariella worthensis*, and its preservation is like that of the other Late Albian material with which it occurs and it cannot be considered reworked. As indicated here, *H. primitivus* n. sp. may be an ancestral form of the genus which is well known in younger Cenomanian rocks.

OCCURRENCE: Holotype and only known specimen from the Pawpaw, BEG locality 17414, 219–T–1, 2 miles southwest of Haslet, Tarrant County, Texas.

REPOSITORY: BEG 35358

Hypoturrilites youngi n. sp.
(Pl. 19, fig. 6)

Hypoturrilites n. sp. YOUNG, 1958, Jour. Paleontology, v. 32, p. 287, Fig. 1–g, Pl. 39, fig. 32

The specimen described by Young from the Trans-Pecos area of west Texas has tuberculation similar to *H. gravesianus* but differs from this and all other species known to the writer by the possession of low ribs which rise from the lower row of small abapical tubercles and pass between the widely spaced large tubercles which are about mid-whorl, adapically on the siphonal margin of the specimen.

". . . sinistral . . . three rows of smaller tubercles . . . faintly clavate; the middle and upper rows are spaced slightly farther apart than are the lower and middle rows. The fourth (upper) row of nodes consists of large tubercles with one tubercle for every three to three and a half tubercles in the other . . . rows . . . base costate from the lowest (abapical) row of tubercles to the umbilicus." (Young, 1958, p. 287)

REMARKS: This species is most similar to *H. tuberculato-plicatus* Sequenza, which has similar mid-whorl ribbing, and to *H. komotai* Yabe, which has ribs extending between the rows of large tubercles. It is difficult to compare *H. youngi* n. sp. with *H. komotai*, as the latter's description appears somewhat different from the figured specimen. *H. youngi* n. sp. bears up to five fine ribs, which extend from the three rows of tubercles in the abapical position to between the single rows of large tubercles adapically.

H. tuberculato-plicatus differs principally in the possession of strong ribs which originate at the large tubercles and extend abapically. The ribs do not extend to the rows of small tubercles as in *H. youngi* n. sp., nor are they as numerous as in equal-sized portions of *H. youngi* n. sp. This unusual ribbing and the unequal spacing of the three rows of small tubercles are the most distinctive features of *H. youngi* n. sp., and even though only a single specimen has been reported, the characteristics serve to distinguish it from all species known to the writer.

OCCURRENCE: Between two draws, north of first large draw south of Cherry Ranch Road, just north of east-west fence of D. Kingston Ranch, northeastern flank of Davis Mountains, Jeff Davis County, Texas. From basal part of Boquillas Formation (Cenomanian), collected by Jess Brundrette.

REPOSITORY: UT 10285

Genus *Turrilites* Lamarck, 1801

This much-used name has restricted use now for a small group of Cenomanian and Lower Turonian species with: "Apical angle acute, shell tightly coiled; ribs weak to strong, with or without 3 or 4 rows of equal numbers of tubercles" (Arkell and others, 1957, p. L222).

Based on Breistroffer's work (1953), three subgenera are now recognized: *Turilites* s. s., *Euturrilites*, and *Mesoturrilites*. Differences are slight, and the normal association of certain species of this group is such that there is only slight biologic and no stratigraphic justification for such a classification. The pattern suggested by Breistroffer and adopted in the *Treatise* is followed for lack of a better substitute.

There are three groups of species which have previously been assigned to *Turrilites* in Texas: those which belong with *Turrilites* s. s., those which are younger than *Turrilites* and which belong with the Nostoceratidae or Diplomoceratidae, and those Albian and Cenomanian species which are classified with other genera of Turrilitidae. The first group includes *T. costatus*, *T. acutus*, *T. dearingi*, and *T. (Euturrilites) scheuchzerianus*. The second includes *T. splendidus*, *T. saundersonum*, *T. varians*, *T. tridens*, and *T. irridens*, the last three of which probably belong to *Hyphantoceras*. The third group includes many of the species described in this report with other of the Turrilitidae genera.

Turrilites (Turrilites) costatus Lamarck
(Figs. 20a, b; Pl. 20, figs. 1, 2, 7, 8)

Turrilites n. sp. aff. *costatus* ADKINS, 1928, Univ. Texas Bull. 2838, p. 215, Pl. 24, fig. 7
Turrilites sp. aff. *costatus* ADKINS, 1928, Univ. Texas Bull. 2838, p. 32
Turrilites aff. *costatus* ADKINS, 1928, Univ. Texas Bull. 2838, p. 29; ADKINS, 1933, Univ. Texas Bull. 3232, p. 434, 438; MOREMAN, 1942, Jour. Paleontology, v. 16, p. 194, 196, 209; ADKINS, 1949, Shreveport Geol. Soc. 17th Ann. Field Trip Guidebook, p. 96; Lozo, 1951, Fondren Sci. Ser., no. 4, p. 156
Turrilites sp. aff. *tuberculatus* ADKINS, 1928, Univ. Texas Bull. 2838, p. 32
Turrilites aff. *tuberculatus* ADKINS, 1928, Univ. Texas Bull. 2838, p. 29; Lozo, 1951, Fondren Sci. Ser., no. 4, p. 156
Turrilites aff. *hugardianus* ADKINS, 1928, Univ. Texas Bull. 2838, p. 29; Lozo, 1951, Fondren Sci. Ser., no. 4, p. 156
Turrilites spp. ADKINS, 1928, Univ. Texas Bull. 2838, p. 29; ADKINS, 1933, Univ. Texas Bull. 3232, p. 438

This well known species was described more than 160 years ago (Lamarck, 1801) and has since been reported from many parts of the world. The synonymy included here refers to only Texas specimens.

Shell helical, sinistral, spiral angle about 25°; 9–11 whorls common on more complete specimens. In all Texas specimens, 18–24 tuberculated rib sets per whorl. Each rib set consists of three distinct tuberculated portions. Adapical set elongated; center set short; abapical set small, often hidden by overlap of younger whorl. Suture of Texas specimen (Fig. 20a) compared with suture of specimen figured by Sharpe (1853–1857) (Fig. 20b).

REMARKS: One of the most interesting aspects of this species is its consistent association with *Turrilites acutus* and *Euturrilites scheuchzerianus*. This association in one collection has been noted in the British Museum, the École des Mines, Paris, in the private collections of General Collignon, Grenoble, the Paleontology Museum of Copenhagen, the Geologisches

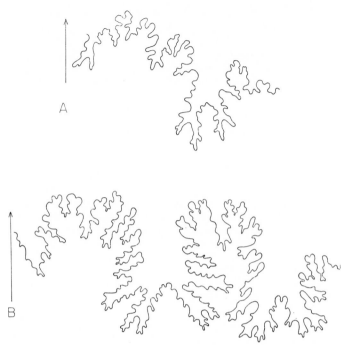

Figure 20. *Sutures of* Turrilites (Turrilites) costatus. (A) Texas specimen (× 3); (B) English specimen, after Sharpe (1853, Pl. XXVII, fig. 16) (Magnification unknown)

Staatsinstitut, Hamburg, and in the collections at the University at Bonn. Recently, Matsumoto (1959) has noted this same association of species in the California Cretaceous. In each case noted, the specimens were collected at the same time from one locality. Many early investigators found this same association (d'Orbigny, 1840; Sharpe, 1853). Reyment (1955) is one of the few writers who has not noted this association.

Differences among these species are rather minor and there are specimens transitional between *E. scheuchzerianus* and *T. costatus* and between the latter and *T. acutus.* Sexual dimorphism or simple population variation could be involved here as there is an ornamentation sequence which extends from the divided ribs of *E. scheuchzerianus* to three discrete tubercles on *T. acutus* through a *T. costatus* stage.

OCCURRENCE: All Texas specimens studied for this report were collected by W. S. Adkins from the Tarrant Formation of the Eagle Ford at exposures on both sides of the old Belton-Temple highway where it crosses Pepper Creek. Moreman (1942) reports this as his locality 3, but he was unable to find specimens of *Turrilites.* A new highway between Belton and Temple has exposed additional outcrops of the basal Eagle Ford, but no additional specimens were collected for this study. Lozo (1951) noted that this species was common at Pepper Creek. Rocks are Late Cenomanian (*subglobosus* zone).

REPOSITORY: BEG 35359, 2410, 21053, 21054, 21056, 21138

Turrilites (Turrilites) acutus Passy
(Pl. 19, fig. 7)

Turrilites n. sp. aff. *desnoyersi* ADKINS, 1928, Univ. Texas Bull. 2838, p. 215, Pl. 24, fig. 6
Turrilites sp. aff. *desnoyersi* ADKINS, 1928, Univ. Texas Bull. 2838, p. 23
Turrilites aff. *desnoyersi* ADKINS, 1928, Univ. Texas Bull. 2838, p. 29; ADKINS, 1933, Univ.
    Texas Bull. 3232, p. 434, 438; MOREMAN, 1942, Jour. Paleontology, v. 16, p. 194, 196, 209;
    Lozo, 1951, Fondren Sci. Ser., no. 4, p. 156
Turrilites aff. *acutus* BÖSE, 1923, Geol. Inst. Mexico Bol., v. 42, p. 151, Pl. 10, figs. 38–41
Turrilites cfr. *wiestii* BÖSE, 1923, Geol. Inst. Mexico Bol., v. 42, p. 150, Pl. 10, figs. 42–47

This synonymy includes only Texas material. Pervinquière (1910) has previously indicated the scope of this species.

Spiral angle, 20°–23°. Three rows tubercles, abapical row less distinct because of whorl overlap but visible. All tubercles bulate, equal number in each row; 14–16 tubercles per whorl. Whorls convex, deep groove between whorls.

REMARKS: The elongated adapical ribs of *T. costatus* and the bulate tubercles of *T. acutus* seem to be most crucial in distinguishing these closely related species.

Of the several specimens from the Texas Cretaceous, only one is from a locality other than the lowest beds of the Tarrant Formation of the Eagle Ford Group. This individual was collected by Gayle Scott from one of the blocks of Cretaceous uplifted by the Palestine salt dome. Powers (1926, p. 49) described the Cretaceous blocks as consisting of Washita ?, Woodbine ?, Eagle Ford, and higher beds. According to Powers (p. 48–49), Stephenson and Lane thought the "Washita ?" was probably ". . . the Buda, the highest formation in the Washita group." Adkins (1933, p. 397) quotes this. It was from this block, about 25 feet thick and below definite Eagle Ford, that the single individual of *T. acutus* was collected. Because of the occurrence of this species in the basal Eagle Ford only 100 miles west of the Palestine outcrop and because of the uncertain age of the beds from which the specimen was collected, it may be best to regard the Palestine material as Tarrant Formation, forced upward by the salt dome.

OCCURRENCE: Basal Tarrant Formation, Temple-Belton road-cuts along Pepper Creek and Washita ? or Tarrant at Palestine salt dome, Texas. Late Cenomanian.

REPOSITORY: BEG 21055; TCU M977

Turrilites (Turrilites) dearingi Stephenson
(Pl. 20, fig. 4)

Turrilites dearingi STEPHENSON, 1952, U.S. Geol. Survey Prof. Paper 242, p. 30, 34, 197, Pl. 44, figs. 6–8

This rare species from the Woodbine Formation is known from a single locality east of Euless in Tarrant County. Stephenson's description follows:

"Shell . . . spirally coiled, sinistral, spiral angle about 21 degrees. Coils closely appressed with the line of contact deeply impressed. Sides of volutions rather strongly convex. Sides ornamented with three rows of prominent conical nodes. On the larger volutions the nodes in each row number 16 to 18, the successive nodes in the 3 rows being alined with each other upward and obliquely forward. The nodes in the lowest row are the smallest and crowd the line of contact with the volution below. The nodes in the upper row which lies a little above the middle of the volution and parallels the upper line of contact are the largest; some of the nodes in this row show a slight tendency to vertical elongation. The slope between the upper row of nodes and the line of contact above is smooth and steep. The base of the spire is flat or very broadly excavated. The sutures are too obscurely preserved for description."

REMARKS: The protrusion of the abapical row of nodes over the whorl contact is a condition present in *T. morrisii* (= *T. carcitanensis* Matheron), but the Texas species is distinct because of the other ornamentation differences.

OCCURRENCE: The two known specimens were collected by J. P. Conlin of Ft. Worth 1.5 miles east of Euless, 0.2 mile north of State Highway 183, Tarrant County, Texas. They were from the Lewisville Member of the Woodbine Formation which has been correlated with the Tarrant Formation of the Eagle Ford. Rocks are Late Cenomanian.

REPOSITORY: Holotype, USNM 105956; paratype Conlin 4134

Subgenus *Turrilites (Euturrilites)* Breistroffer

This subgenus was proposed for those species of *Turrilites* which are nontuberculate and with simple ribs depressed or divided in the middle, especially on the early whorls. Those specimens which have been placed in this taxon have more or less complete undivided ribs on the portion of the shell which represents the mature individual.

Turrilites (Euturrilites) scheuchzerianus (Bosc)
(Pl. 20, figs. 3, 5, 6)

? *Turrilites scheuchzeri* var. *mexicana* Bösе, 1923, Geol. Inst. Mexico Bol., v. 42, p. 145, Pl. 10, figs. 20, 21

A single specimen in the Texas collections and several in the collections from Mexico seem more closely related to *E. scheuchzerianus* than to *T. costatus*. None of the specimens are well preserved. Ornamentation consists of broad nontuberculate ribs which are divided on the early portions, the divided part being separated by a depressed area at about the mid-flank of the whorl. Portions of the ribs have been removed by weathering and the specimens from Mexico may well be weathered *Mariella*. The Texas specimen has a few unweathered ribs which show the normal *E. scheuchzerianus* pattern.

REMARKS: As has been mentioned, this species occurs with the species of *Turrilites* s. s. and is very closely related. Separation of species is on the basis of no tubercles on *Euturrilites,* but the division of the ribs into two portions appears to be the first step toward acquiring distinct nodes or tubercles.

OCCURRENCE: Lowest part of the Tarrant Formation of the Eagle Ford, associated with *T. costatus* and *T. acutus,* on the Temple-Belton highway along Pepper Creek, Texas. Late Cenomanian.

REPOSITORY: BEG 21054

Genus *Carthaginites* Pervinquière, 1907

Carthaginites sp. ADKINS, 1928, Univ. Texas Bull. 2838, p. 204, 216; ADKINS AND LOZO, 1951, Fondren Sci. Ser., no. 4, p. 153
Carthaginites sp. aff. *kerimensis* ADKINS, 1928, Univ. Texas Bull. 2838, p. 26

This is the second of the two genera which have been reported from the Texas Cretaceous, but whose presence is not confirmed. The report of Adkins in 1928 includes no satisfactory locality or repository data. Except for references to the fact that the specimen or specimens in question were obtained from the Buda Formation at Austin, nothing has been published about this unique genus in Texas. None of the Texas repositories have record of the material reported by Adkins.

Arkell and others (1957, p. L222) list Texas as one of the two localities from which this genus has been obtained, but Wright has informed the writer that this reference was based on Adkins' 1928 report and not on additional material or information.

J. P. Conlin of Ft. Worth, has summarized the dilemma in a letter to the writer (1960):

"The thing cited by Adkins as *Carthaginites* . . . might be an extremely flat-sided *Plesioturrilites bosquensis* as I collected a few that were suggestive, from Waco."

Pervinquière (1907, Pl. IV, figs. 18, 19) illustrates a spiral groove along the middle of an otherwise smooth whorl flank on the type of the genus. Flat *Plesioturrilites* with groove are known, and perhaps *Carthaginites* from Africa belongs with *Plesioturrilites* species.

Superfamily SCAPHITACEAE Meek, 1876

Family SCAPHITIDAE Meek, 1876

This well known group of Upper Albian to Upper Maestrichtian ammonoids is divided into two subfamilies: Scaphitinae, which includes *Scaphites* s. s., and the Otoscaphitinae, which includes two unusual genera whose evolution can be traced in detail in the Texas Cretaceous.

The scaphitids have an evolute to involute shell followed by a shaft and terminal hook. Various aperture modifications are taxonomically important, and ornamentation consists of ribs and tubercles.

This family is represented by more than 30 species in the Texas Cretaceous, but, with the exception of the Turonian Otoscaphitinae, only the Albian and Cenomanian species are here described.

Subfamily SCAPHITINAE Meek, 1876

". . . more or less involute camerate whorls . . . followed by a long or short shaft with terminal hook . . . aperture may be simple, collared, and constricted; . . . lappets, if present, dorsal only." (Arkell and others, 1957, p. L228)

This group originated during the Late Albian, and Reeside (1927), Spath (1937), and Cobban (1951) have summarized much data.

Eleven genera, all of which were originally referred to a single genus, are now recognized. In the Texas Cretaceous rocks, four species of Albian-Cenomanian Scaphitinae are known, and several times this number are present in the Turonian and younger rocks. Moreman (1942), Stephenson (1941), and others have described the younger scaphitids.

Scaphites worthensis Adkins and Winton
(Pl. 22, fig. 5)

Scaphites sp. B WINTON AND ADKINS, 1920, Univ. Texas Bull. 1931, p. 22

Scaphites worthensis ADKINS AND WINTON, 1920, Univ. Texas Bull. 1945, p. 20, 36, Pl. 7, figs. 1, 2; SCOTT, 1926, Univ. Grenoble Thèse, Faculty Sci., p. 62, 150–151; ADKINS, 1928, Univ. Texas Bull. 2838, p. 257; ADKINS, 1933, Univ. Texas Bull. 3232, p. 367; SPATH, 1937, Palaeont. Soc. London Mon., pt. 12, p. 502

Scaphites aequalis et *S. obliquus* SCOTT, 1926, Univ. Grenoble Thèse, Faculty Sci., p. 149–152

Macroscaphites ? *worthensis* REESIDE, 1927, U.S. Geol. Survey Prof. Paper 150–B, p. 36

Worthoceras worthense COBBAN, 1951, U.S. Geol. Survey Prof. Paper 239, p. 6

This Late Albian *Scaphites*, the earliest known in North America and probably as early as *Eoscaphites circularis* from the Late Albian of Europe, was formerly a common fossil in the upper Duck Creek, and Adkins and Winton called their "Zone 16" of the Washita the *Scaphites worthensis* zone, based on its general abundance. Perkins (1961) does not list this species in his faunal study of the Duck Creek in north Texas, and the writer did not collect a specimen in the Texas area during 1957–1960.

"Coiled portion is small, involute and closely coiled . . . a medium sized umbilicus . . . The inflated portion is slightly concave on its ventral margin, so that it is thickest near the middle. Its apertural end is constricted and narrowed ventrally so that the shell bends dorsally. . . . the extended portion is broadly excavated dorsally . . . the shell bears fine continuous ribs, branched or unbranched. The ribs are of two lengths, the longer ones reaching the umbilical margin. The shorter ones arise just lateral to the umbilical margin." (Adkins and Winton, 1920, p. 36)

REMARKS: Scott (1926) believed that this species, along with *S. hilli* from the Pawpaw, was a junior synonym of "*S. aequalis* and *S. obliquus*" but Adkins (1928, p. 257) subtly pointed out that ". . . it is likewise distinct from *S. aequalis,* unless one considers all scaphites to belong to the same species."

Spath (1937, p. 502) considered *S. worthensis* distinct from his Gault species and based this reasoning, in part at least, on the doubtful reference of Reeside (1927) of this species to *Macroscaphites,* ". . . so that it must be a distinct species."

Cobban (1951) called the ". . . oldest described scaphite (in America) *Worthoceras worthense*" in obvious reference to *S. worthensis,* but justifiably confused with the host of "*worthoceras*" and similar specific endings in the literature of Texas Cretaceous cephalopods (*e.g., Hamulina worthense, Worthoceras worthense, Pervinquieria worthensis, Summantelliceras worthense, Mariella worthensis,* etc.).

S. worthensis may be considered to be most logically placed with *Eoscaphites* (Breistroffer, 1947) because of its age, but its morphologic characters are intermediate between such species as *E. circularis* and *S. hilli. S. worthensis* is from the Duck Creek, which is considered to be equivalent to the *varicosum-auritus* subzones of the Gault. *E. circularis,* from the *varicosum* interval at Kent, has been considered the oldest *Scaphites* in Europe.

The Texas *S. worthensis* lacks tubercles and possesses simple ribs as in *Eoscaphites,* but the early whorls are not nearly as evolute as those of *Eoscaphites,* and there is a prominent apertural constriction on *S. worthensis,* a feature characteristic of *Scaphites* s. s.

OCCURRENCE: Holotype from 3 miles southwest of Ft. Worth, Texas, from upper marly part of Duck Creek Formation. According to Adkins and Winton (1920), species ranges into the lower Duck Creek and high as the Cenomanian Mainstreet Formation. Late Albian (*varicosum-auritus*) to Early Cenomanian (*varians*).

REPOSITORY: BEG 20989, holotype. Many unnumbered specimens in the Renfro collections, USNM, from the Duck Creek and Weno.

Scaphites hilli Adkins and Winton

(Fig. 21a; Pl. 21, fig. 4, Pl. 22, figs. 4, 6, 7–9, Pl. 4, figs. 2–4)

Scaphites sp. A. WINTON AND ADKINS, 1920, Univ. Texas Bull. 1931, p. 21, 69
Scaphites hilli ADKINS AND WINTON, 1920, Univ. Texas Bull. 1945, p. 28, 37–38, Pl. 7, figs. 3–6; WINTON AND ADKINS, 1920, Univ. Texas Bull. 1931, p. 21; ADKINS, 1920, Univ. Texas Bull. 1856, p. 51, 79–84, Pl. 2, figs. 1–12; WINTON, 1925, Univ. Texas Bull. 2544, Pl. 6, fig. 3; SCOTT, 1926, Univ. Grenoble Thèse, Faculty Sci., p. 151–152; REESIDE, 1927, U.S. Geol. Survey Prof. Paper 150–B, p. 30; ADKINS, 1928, Univ. Texas Bull. 2838, p. 24, 257, Pl. 20, figs. 1, 3, 7; BÖSE, 1928, Univ. Texas Bull. 2748, p. 146; SPATH, 1937, Palaeont. Soc. London Mon., pt. 12, p. 507; BREISTROFFER, 1947, Travaux Lab. Géol. Grenoble, t. 26, p. 66; COBBAN, 1951, U.S. Geol. Survey Prof. Paper 239, p. 6
"*Scaphites aequalis* et *S. obliquus*" SCOTT, 1926, Univ. Grenoble Thèse, Faculty Sci., p. 149–152

Adkins and Winton described this species in a paper published in January of 1920, and in November of the year Adkins described the same species in much greater detail.

"Small, subglobose, inner volutions regularly coiled, closely embracing . . . umbilicus narrow . . . extended body portion very little unrolled . . . branched . . . and unbranched ribs. . . ."

Ribs thicken into dorsal lateral tubercles on body portion. Suture illustrated (Fig. 21a).

REMARKS: Before this species had been described for a full year, Adkins (1920) indicated some uncertainty as to whether or not the species should be placed with *S. aequalis* or *S. obliquus.* Scott (1926) believed that *S. hilli* was a junior synonym of "*S. aequalis* et *S. obliquus.*" Spath (1937) discussed the relationship of the Albian species and Cenomanian types such as *S. aequalis* and pointed out the resemblance that *S. hilli* had to *S. simplex* (p. 502). Spath believed that the two species were distinct because of ". . . a different body-chamber, a wider umbilicus . . ." and in addition, he put great value in the sutural differences. The body chamber is rarely preserved on the Texas specimens, but on those examined it was noted that there is an umbilical thickening or covering on *S. hilli* which seems to be consistently different from *S. simplex.* Actually, Spath's description of *S. simplex* (1937, p. 502) is very similar to *S. hilli* but the tubercles on the body chamber and the umbilical covering provided by the body chamber of *S. hilli* are different from *S. simplex.* *S. simplex* is figured as Figures 1–3 and 5 of Plate 21 in order to have comparison with *S. hilli.*

OCCURRENCE: Late Albian Pawpaw Formation and Mainstreet Formation; holotype from base of Pawpaw, Sycamore Creek, Ft. Worth, Texas.

REPOSITORY: BEG 20986, holotype; BEG 20989; Conlin 8542, 8546, 8548, 8549

Scaphites bosquensis Böse

(Fig. 21b; Pl. 4, figs. 1, 8, 12)

Scaphites bosquensis BÖSE, 1928, Univ. Texas Bull. 2748, p. 148, 154, 224–225, Pl. 7, figs. 1–6; ADKINS, 1928, Univ. Texas Bull. 2838, p. 25, 257–258; COBBAN, 1951, U.S. Geol. Survey Prof. Paper 239, p. 6

Holotype small, globose, venter flatter than dorsum. Whorls tightly coiled, umbilicus deep and little wider than *S. Simplex* and *S. hilli.* Simple and bifurcating ribs present, no indication of tubercles. Body chamber missing. Suture illustrated (Fig. 21b).

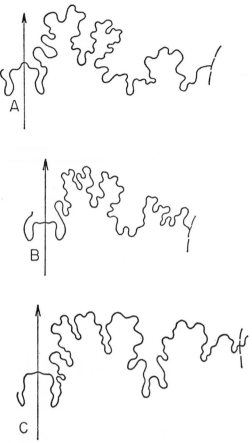

Figure 21. *Sutures of Family Scaphitidae.* (A) *Scaphites hilli* (× 4.5); (B) *Scaphites bosquensis* (× 4.5); (C) *Scaphites subevolutus* (× 4.5)

REMARKS: This species was established by Böse for a single poorly preserved specimen with no shaft or body chamber. The holotype is crushed, and without diagnostic characteristics of the body chamber and aperture it is difficult to determine specific identification.

Böse pointed out that *S. bosquensis* was of the group of *S. aequalis* and was similar to *S. hilli.* The coiled fragment is also similar to other Cenomanian and Albian *Scaphites,* and without additional material it is not possible to determine the validity of *S. bosquensis.*

OCCURRENCE: Early Cenomanian Del Rio Formation; holotype from east bank of South Bosque River, 2 miles south of South Bosque, McLennan County, Texas.

REPOSITORY: BEG 21039, holotype

Scaphites subevolutus Böse
(Fig. 21c; Pl. 22, figs. 1–3)

Scaphites subevolutus BÖSE, 1928, Univ. Texas Bull. 2748, p. 26, 91, 154, 158–159, 225–229, Pl. 7, figs. 7–30, Pl. 18, fig. 8; ADKINS, 1928, Univ. Texas Bull. 2838, p. 25, 259, Pl. 23, fig. 10; SPATH, 1937, Palaeont. Soc. London Mon., pt. 12, p. 500; 1942, pt. 15, p. 719; COBBAN, 1951, U.S. Geol. Survey Prof. Paper 239, p. 6; WRIGHT, 1953, Ann. Mag. Nat. History, v. 6, ser. 2, p. 476

". . . Shell discoidal, . . . evolute . . . flanks well rounded . . . very wide . . . umbilicus. . . . The three smallest whorls are entirely smooth; the first half of the fourth whorl carries about nine more or less elevated ribs." (Böse, 1928, p. 225–226)

Ribbing increases in number and strength to preserved outer whorls. Lateral swelling of ribs prominent.

REMARKS: This species seems to be closely related to *S. evolutus* Pervinquière, known from Algeria and Madagascar. Spath (1937) discussed the very evolute coiling of this species in his comparison of *Eoscaphites circularis* but emphasized that the evolute coiling was the major and most important similarity of the two species.

Wright (1953) suggested that *S. subevolutus* and *S. evolutus* may belong with *Otoscaphites* of the Otoscaphitinae. His idea is based on the evolute coiling and ornamentation as well as age, as all of these factors overlap with the Otoscaphitinae. Wright emphasized (p. 476), however, that ". . . better specimens are needed before their position can be ascertained."

Among the specimens of this species available, there are none which have the shaft or hook, and this fact limits their understanding. Böse (1928) recognized this in his original description and was particularly concerned with sutural differences between his species and *Scaphites* s. s. (Fig. 21c).

OCCURRENCE: Del Rio Formation, Early Cenomanian *(varians)*; holotype from 4.5 miles south of McGregor, Texas. The species is known from numerous localities in the central Texas area.

REPOSITORY: BEG 21040, holotype

Subfamily OTOSCAPHITINAE Wright, 1953

Wright's fine discussion of this subfamily (1953) was adopted in the *Treatise on Invertebrate Paleontology,* 1957, and little additional information has been published.

Wright considered this group to be an early branch of the scaphitid line which evolved in parallel to the Scaphitinae but with marked differences. Large lateral lappets with weaker ornamentation than in the Scaphitinae characterize this group.

Evolution of the Otoscaphitinae probably followed from an *Eoscaphites* or even a *S. worthensis* ancestor in the Late Albian through *Worthoceras platydorsum, W. vermiculum, W. gibbosum,* and *Otoscaphites minutes,* in the Cenomanian and Turonian. This sequence is known in detail only in the Texas Cretaceous rocks, and it may be that the center of evolution of this group, early in its history, was North America.

Only two genera, *Worthoceras* and *Otoscaphites,* are presently recognized and both have been found in Europe as well as North America. All known species are small and not common in the Texas Cretaceous.

Genus *Worthoceras* Adkins, 1928

Adkins established this name for those species he described as follows:

". . . initial portion a planospiral coil, followed by a straight limb, which connects by a bend to a shorter and thicker straight limb subparallel to the first but not touching it. Ribs and tubercles reduced or absent."

Arkell and others (1957) have further pointed out that long straight lappets on the aperture are characteristic of the genus. These lappets are commonly broken from the fossils, however. Five species ranging from Late Albian to Early Turonian are now recognized. Four of these in the Texas Cretaceous are here described.

Wright (1953) has indicated that the early member of the Otoscaphitinae evolved in parallel to the Scaphitinae but that it never obtained such a complex suture or ornamentation. The more or less complete sequence of *Worthoceras* species found in the Texas rocks seems to confirm Wright's ideas that this genus and its species constitute an evolutionary series, and that the various species are not occasional aberrant offshoots of the Scaphitinae as suggested by Spath (1937, p. 498).

Two specimens (BYU 403, 404) were collected from the Chispa Summit, Eagle Ford equivalent in west Texas, which are not generically identifiable but clearly referable to the group *Worthoceras-Otoscaphites.* Adkins (1931) referred to *Scaphites* in his collection from the same area.

Worthoceras platydorsum (Scott)
(Pl. 23, fig. 4)

Macroscaphites platydorsus SCOTT, 1924, Texas Christian Univ. Quart., v. 1, p. 18–19, Pls. 5, 6, Pl. 9, fig. 6

Worthoceras platydorsus ADKINS, 1928, Univ. Texas Bull. 2838, p. 219; ARKELL, KUMMEL, AND WRIGHT, *in* MOORE, 1957, Treatise Invertebrate Paleontology: Geol. Soc. America and Univ. Kansas Press, pt. L, p. L231

Worthoceras platydorsum MOREMAN, 1942, Jour. Paleontology, v. 16, p. 215; WRIGHT, 1953, Ann. Mag. Nat. History, v. 6, ser. 2, p. 474

This poorly understood species is characterized by a flat dorsum and a shell which expands rapidly to large size on the final straight shaft and hook. It is involute and ribbing is very fine. The suture is less complicated than that of *W. worthense* (Adkins), and this feature has been used by Scott (1924), Adkins (1928), and Wright (1953) for distinction. Marginal lappets may be present.

REMARKS: This species was described in considerable detail by Scott (1924), but its taxonomic status has only recently been resolved (Wright, 1953). The location of the holotype is not known to the writer and only a few fragments have been available for this study. The figured holotype was not complete and the critical feature of marginal lappets has not been confirmed. Wright (1953, p. 474–475) concluded:

"Although I know of no specimens of *W. platydorsum* with mouth-border preserved I have no hesitation in regarding the lappets as a generic character, for *W. worthense* differs very little from the type-species except in having a slightly more complicated suture."

The species occurs in the early or middle Late Albian, several hundred feet stratigraphically lower than the Late Albian *W. worthense*. The holotype was supposedly placed at Texas Christian University, but this cannot be firmly established. Without the type, it is difficult to determine whether or not it is a junior synonym of *W. worthense*. Only very minute coiled stages of this species have been studied and the difference between them and similar parts of *W. worthense* is difficult to detect.

OCCURRENCE: Holotype from upper Duck Creek Formation, about 3 miles north of Denison, Texas. Present location unknown. Other specimens from the upper part of the Duck Creek of the Ft. Worth area. Late Albian (*varicosum-auritus*).

REPOSITORY: TCU 1136

Worthoceras worthense (Adkins)
(Fig. 22a; Pl. 23, figs. 1–3, 5–10)

Hamulina worthensis ADKINS, 1920, Univ. Texas Bull. 1856, p. 51, 71–74, Fig. 3, Pl. 2, figs. 23–26; SCOTT, 1924, Texas Christian Univ. Quart., v. 1, p. 18; BÖSE, 1928, Univ. Texas Bull. 2748, p. 146

Worthoceras worthense ADKINS, 1928, Univ. Texas Bull. 2838, p. 24, 219–220, Pl. 20, fig. 8; ADKINS, 1933, Univ. Texas Bull. 3232, p. 381; SPATH, 1937, Palaeont. Soc. London Mon., pt. 12, p. 498; 1942, pt. 15, p. 719; WRIGHT, 1953, Ann. Mag. Nat. History, v. 6, ser. 2, p. 474–475

". . . two non-contiguous straight limbs united by a single curve . . ." (Adkins, 1920, p. 71), ribbing reduced to absent, earlier parts rather smooth but with indication of 4–6 rows of very small nodes obliquely arranged on lateral portion. Dorsum flat. Holotype lacks initial coiled part found on other specimens. Wright (1953, p. 474) reported that J. P. Conlin had found a specimen with the base of a lateral lappet preserved. Suture illustrated (Fig. 22a).

REMARKS: The specimens labeled *W. platydorsum* from the Duck Creek in the Scott collections at Texas Christian University are smaller than the specimens of *W. worthense*. This feature, along with a more simple suture, was noted by Scott as distinguishing features of *W. platydorsum* as compared with *W. worthense*.

OCCURRENCE: Holotype from Adkins locality 714, 4½ miles southeast of Ft. Worth, one-quarter mile south of Railway Bridge over Sycamore Creek. From Pawpaw Formation, Late

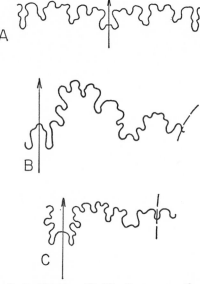

Figure 22. *Sutures of Family Scaphitidae.* (A) *Worthoceras worthense* (× 4.5); (B) *Wortho-ceras gibbosum* (× 4.5); (C) *Otoscaphites minutus* (× 4.5)

Albian *(dispar-perinflatum).* Other specimens have been obtained from the Pawpaw of most localities in north Texas.

REPOSITORY: BEG 20994, holotype; BEG 20995, 20996, paratypes; TCU 1082

Worthoceras vermiculum (Shumard)
(Pl. 4, figs. 9–11)

Scaphites vermiculus SHUMARD, 1860, Acad. Sci. St. Louis Trans., v. 1, no. 4, p. 594–595; WHITE, 1883, U.S. Geol. Survey Terr. 12th Ann. Rept., 1878, pt. 1, p. 39, Pl. 18, fig. 8; HILL, 1889b, Texas Geol. Survey Bull. 4, p. 24; REESIDE, 1927, U.S. Geol. Survey Prof. Paper 150–B, p. 35; ADKINS, 1928, Univ. Texas Bull. 2838, p. 220, 259–260; ADKINS, 1933, Univ. Texas Bull, 3232, p. 432; WRIGHT, 1953, Ann. Mag. Nat. History, v. 6, ser. 2, p. 474
Macroscaphites vermiculus MEEK, 1876, U.S. Geol. Survey Terr. 9th Ann. Rept., p. 419
Worthoceras vermiculum MOREMAN, 1942, Jour. Paleontology, v. 16, p. 214–215, Fig. 2p, Pl. 34, figs. 12, 13
Worthoceras vermiculus WRIGHT, 1953, Ann. Mag. Nat History, v. 6, ser. 2, p. 474–475

Moreman (1942) figured the neotype but did not describe the species. Shumard's (1860, p. 594–595) description follows:

"Shell, small, ovate, length not quite one-third greater than the height; sides gently convex, dorsum strongly rounded, ventral side flattened, obtusely sub-angulated at junction with sides; body-whorl slightly sinuate, very gradually enlarging, and produced horizontally for a distance equal to the diameter of the regularly coiled part, then curved backwards so as to bring the aperture to within a short distance of the middle of the long diameter of the shell; volutions of spire partially embracing, leaving a deep umbilicus in which three or four coils are visible; surface marked with a few obscure, transverse folds, and fine striae of increase."

REMARKS: Moreman (1942) established a neotype for this species. Shumard (1860) collected the holotype from septaria of the marly clay in Grayson County, about 4 miles north of Sherman. This has been considered to be Eagle Ford.

This species, along with *W. gibbosum,* both from the Eagle Ford, are the last of the *Worthoceras* line.

OCCURRENCE: Neotype from the Britton Formation of the Eagle Ford (Early Turonian, *plenus*). BEG locality 70–T–8.

REPOSITORY: BEG 19827, neotype

Worthoceras gibbosum Moreman
(Fig. 22b; Pl. 4, figs. 13–15)

Worthoceras gibbosum MOREMAN, 1942, Jour. Paleontology, v. 16, p. 215, Fig. 2q, Pl. 34, figs. 7, 8; WRIGHT, 1953, Ann. Mag. Nat. History, v. 6, ser. 2, p. 475

The last known survivor of the *Worthoceras* s. s. group is also the largest.

". . . whorl depressed; venter rounded; flanks convex; initial portion a planospiral coil, followed by a straight portion, which connects to a shorter limb subparallel to the first but not touching it, and continuing to within 1 mm of the coiled portion; body whorl gradually increasing in width from the initial portion to the aperture; volutions of the coil embracing, leaving a deep umbilicus in which three or four coils are visible; umbilicus comparatively broad, being one-third of the diameter of the coiled portion. Surface marked by the very obscure ribs or striae which are devoid of tubercles." (Moreman, 1942, p. 215)

Suture figured (Fig. 22b).

REMARKS: Wright (1953, p. 475) has indicated that *W. gibbosum*

". . . with more inflated whorl section, shorter shaft, which is rounded not straight, and a rather more frilled suture than the other species . . . leads directly to the next genus," *Otoscaphites*.

This terminal member of the *Worthoceras* group stands intermediate in characters between the typical *Worthoceras* and its descendant *Otoscaphites*. Its curved shaft (straight in *Worthoceras*) and moderately ribbed spire (smooth in *Worthoceras*) are distinctive.

OCCURRENCE: Middle part of Britton Formation of Eagle Ford (Early Turonian, *plenus*). BEG locality 70–T–8.

REPOSITORY: BEG 19812, holotype

Genus *Otoscaphites* Wright, 1953

This genus is characterized by an evolute shell with a curved shaft and hook which are quite open. Ribs range from weak to strong, and long lateral lappets are present. The presence of ornamentation and a curved shaft on *Otoscaphites*, and their absence on *Worthoceras* are distinguishing.

Otoscaphites is found from the Lower Turonian to the Coniacian in Europe, Japan, and North America. Recently, Cobban and Gryc (1961) have described a new species from Alaska.

Only a single species is known from Texas, although Wright (1953) suggests that *Scaphites subevolutus* Böse, known only from a heavily ribbed spire, may belong to the *Otoscaphites* group.

Otoscaphites minutus (Moreman)
(Fig. 22c; Pl. 4, figs. 5–7)

Scaphites minutus MOREMAN, 1942, Jour. Paleontology, v. 16, p. 216, Fig. 2s, Pl. 34, figs. 9, 10; COBBAN, 1951, U.S. Geol. Survey Prof. Paper 239, p. 23; WRIGHT, 1953, Ann. Mag. Nat. History, v. 6, ser. 2, p. 475

Shell consists of coiled portion and straight shaft followed by terminal hook which is only few mm above the initial coiled portion; umbilicus wide, well-preserved lappets, collared aperture. Ribs low but continuous across venter, tubercles present on ventrolateral margin. Suture illustrated (Fig. 22c).

REMARKS: In a footnote Wright pointed out that J. P. Conlin of Ft. Worth had found a specimen of Scaphitidae with well-preserved lappets and collared aperture which confirmed his ideas that this species belonged with his new genus *Otoscaphites*. This is the earliest known *Otoscaphites* and it probably gave rise to the later Cretaceous species known in Europe, North America, and Japan. Moreman's description was based on a single well-preserved specimen, and few individuals have been collected until the present.

OCCURRENCE: Britton Formation of the Eagle Ford (Early Turonian, *plenus*). BEG locality 154–T–13.

REPOSITORY: BEG 21040

REFERENCES CITED

Adkins, W. S., 1920, The Weno and Pawpaw formations of the Texas Comanchean: Univ. Texas Bull. 1856, p. 1–172, 13 figs., 11 pls.

—— 1928, Handbook of Texas Cretaceous fossils: Univ. Texas Bull. 2838, 385 p., 37 pls.

—— 1931, Some Upper Cretaceous ammonites in western Texas: Univ. Texas Bull. 3101, p. 35–72, 2 figs., 4 pls.

—— 1933, The Mesozoic systems in Texas, p. 239–518, Figs. 13–27 in Sellards, E. H., Adkins, W. S., Scott, W., and Plummer, F. B., The geology of Texas: Univ. Texas Bull. 3232, 1007 p., 54 figs., 10 pls.

Adkins, W. S., and Winton, W. M., 1920, Paleontological correlation of the Fredericksburg and Washita formations in north Texas: Univ. Texas Bull. 1945, 128 p., 6 figs., 22 pls.

Anderson, F. M., 1958, Upper Cretaceous of the Pacific Coast: Geol. Soc. America Mem. 71, 378 p., 3 figs., 75 pls., 8 tables

Arkell, W. J., Kummel, B., and Wright, C. W., 1957, Mesozoic Ammonoidea, p. L80–L465 in Moore, R. C., Editor, Treatise on invertebrate paleontology, Part L, Mollusca 4: Geol. Soc. America and Univ. Kansas Press, 490 p., 558 figs.

Astier, M. J., 1850, Catalogue descriptif des Ancyloceras appartenant a l'étage Néocomien d'escragnolles et des Basses-Alps: Annales Sci. Physiques et Naturelles, d'Agric. et Indust. de Lyon, t. 111, 2d. ser., p. 435–456, Pls. 15–23

Böse, Emil, 1923, Algunas faunas Cretacicas de Zacatecas, Durango y Geurrero: Geol. Inst. Mexico Bol., v. 42, 219 p., 19 pls.

—— 1928, Cretaceous ammonites from Texas and northern Mexico: Univ. Texas Bull. 2748, p. 143–312, 18 pls.

Breistroffer, Maurice, 1940, Révision des ammonites du Vraconien de Salazac (Card) et considérations générales sur le cous-étage albien: Travaux Lab. Géol. Grenoble, t. 22, p. 73–171

—— 1947, Sur les zones d'ammonites dans l'albien de France et a' Angleterre: Travaux Lab. Géol. Grenoble, t. 26, p. 17–104

—— 1953, L'évolution des Turrilitidés albiens et cénomaniens: Comptes Rendus Acad. Sci. France, t. 237, p. 1349–1351

Clark, D. L., 1958, Anisoceras and Ancyloceras from the Texas Cretaceous: Jour. Paleontology, v. 32, p. 1076–1081, 1 fig., Pls. 139, 140

—— 1962, Paedomorphosis, acceleration, and caenogenesis in the evolution of Texas Cretaceous ammonoids: Evolution, v. 16, p. 300–305, 3 figs.

—— 1963, The heteromorph Phlycticrioceras in the Texas Cretaceous: Jour. Paleontology, v. 37, p. 429–432, 1 fig., Pl. 52

Cobban, W. A., 1951, Scaphitoid cephalopods of the Colorado Group: U.S. Geol. Survey Prof. Paper 239, 42 p., 4 figs., 21 pls.

—— 1958a, Two new species of Baculites from the Western Interior region: Jour. Paleontology, v. 32, p. 660–665, 1 fig., 2 pls., 2 tables

—— 1958b, Late Cretaceous fossil zones of the Powder River Basin, Wyoming and Montana: Wyo. Geol. Assoc., Guidebook, 13th Ann. Field Conf., p. 114–119

Cobban, W. A., and Gryc, George, 1961, Ammonites from the Seabee Formation (Cretaceous) of northern Alaska: Jour. Paleontology, v. 35, p. 176–190, 2 figs., 2 pls., 5 tables

Collignon, Maurice, 1932, Les ammonites pyriteuses de l'albien supérieur du Mont Raynaud à Madagascar: Annales Géol. Ser. Mines, f. 2, p. 5–36, 4 pls.

Conrad, T. A., 1855, Descriptions of eighteen new Cretaceous and Tertiary fossils: Phila. Acad. Nat. Sci. Proc. 7, p. 265–268

—— 1857, Descriptions of Cretaceous and Tertiary fossils in Emory, W. H., Editor, Report of the United States and Mexican Boundary Survey: 34th U.S. Cong., 1st sess., Senate Executive Doc. 108, v. 20, and House Executive Doc. 135, v. 1, pt. 2, p. 141–147, 21 pls.

Cragin, F. W., 1893, A contribution to the invertebrate paleontology of the Texas Cretaceous: Geol. Survey Texas 4th Ann. Rept., p. 141–294, Pls. 26–46

—— 1900, Buchiceras (Sphenodiscus) belviderensis and its varieties: Colorado Coll. Studies, v. 8, p. 27–31

De Beer, G. R., 1958, Embryos and ancestors: Oxford, Clarendon Press, 197 p., 19 figs.

Dubourdieu, G., 1953, Ammonites nouvelles des monts du Mellègue: Algeria, Serv. Carte Géologie Bull., 1st ser., no. 16, 76 p.

Grossouvre, A. de, 1894, Recherches sur la craie supérieure. Pt. 2, Paléontologie, les ammonites de la craie supérieure: Mém. Carte Géol. France, 264 p., 39 pls.

Hill, R. T., 1889a, Paleontology of the Cretaceous formations of Texas: Univ. Texas, School Geology, pt. 1, 6 p., 3 pls.

—— 1889b, A preliminary annotated check list of the Cretaceous invertebrate fossils of Texas, accompanied by a short description of the lithology and stratigraphy of the system: Geol. Survey Texas Bull. 4, xxxi + 57 p.

—— 1901, Geography and geology of the Black and Grand Prairies: U.S. Geol. Survey 21st Ann. Rept., pt. 7, 666 p., 80 figs., 71 pls.

Hyatt, Alpheus, 1894, Phylogeny of acquired characteristics: Am. Philos. Soc. Proc., v. 32, p. 349–647

—— 1900, Cephalopoda, p. 502–592 in von Zittel, K. A., Editor, Text-book of paleontology: London and New York, v. 1, pt. 2, 838 p., 1594 figs.

Kellum, Lewis B., 1956, Cretaceous invertebrates of the Aurora Limestone (Mexico): Michigan Acad. Sci. Papers, 1955, v. 41, p. 205–231

Lamarck, J. B. P. A. de M. de, 1801, System des animaux sans vertèbres: Paris, J. B. Lamarck, Chez Deterville, 432 p.

Lasswitz, Rudolf von, 1904, Die Kreide-Ammoniten von Texas: Geol. Palaeont. Abh., new ser., v. 10, heft 6, p. 223–259, 8 pls.

Laughbaum, L. R., 1960, A paleoecologic study of the upper Denton Formation, Tarrant, Denton, and Cooke counties, Texas: Jour. Paleontology, v. 34, p. 1183–1197, 3 figs.

Loeblich, A. R., Jr., and Tappan, Helen, 1961, Cretaceous planktonic Foraminifera. Pt. 1, Cenomanian: Micropaleontology, v. 7, p. 257–304, 8 pls.

Lozo, F. E., Jr., Editor, 1951, The Woodbine and adjacent strata of the Waco area of central Texas: Fondren Sci. Ser., no. 4, 163 p.

Marcou, Jules, 1858, Geology of North America: Zurich, Zürcher and Furrer, 144 p., 9 pls.

Matsumoto, Tatsuro, 1959–1960, Upper Cretaceous ammonites of California: Kyushu Univ., Mem. Fac. Sci., ser D: pt. 1 (v. 8, no. 4, 1959), 171 p., 85 figs., 45 pls.; pt. 2 (special v. 1, 1959), 172 p., 80 figs., 41 pls., pt. 3 (special v. 2, 1960), 204 p., 20 figs., 2 pls.

Meek, F. B., 1876, A report on the invertebrate Cretaceous and Tertiary fossils of the upper Missouri country: U.S. Geol. Survey Terr. 9th Ann. Rept., 629 p., 45 pls.

Moreman, W. L., 1927, Fossil zones of the Eagle Ford of north Texas: Jour. Paleontology, v. 1, p. 89–101, 1 fig., Pls. 13–16

—— 1942, Paleontology of the Eagle Ford Group of north and central Texas: Jour. Paleontology, v. 16, p. 192–220, 2 figs., Pls. 31–34

Murphy, M. A., and Rodda, P. U., 1960, Mollusca of the Cretaceous Bald Hills Formation of California: Jour. Paleontology, v. 34, p. 835–858, 2 figs., 7 pls.

Nowak, J., 1911, Untersuchungen über die Cephalopoden der oberen Kreide in Polen: Acad. Sci. Cracovie (B) Bull., p. 547–589, 2 pls.

—— 1916, Zur Bedeutung von Scaphites für die Gliederung der Oberkreide: Wien, Verh. Geol. Reichsanst., no. 3, p. 55–67

Orbigny, Alcide d', 1840–1842, Paléontologie francaise; Terrains crétacés. 1, Céphalopodes: Paris, A. Bertrand, V. Masson, 662 p., 148 pls.

Perkins, B. F., 1961, Biostratigraphic studies in the Comanche (Cretaceous) Series of northern Mexico and Texas: Geol. Soc. America Mem. 83, 138 p., 26 figs., 34 pls., 2 tables

Pervinquière, L., 1907, Études de paléontologie tunisienne. 1, Céphalopodes des terrains secondaires; système crétacique: Carte Geol. Tunisie, p. 43–428, 27 pls.

—— 1910, Sur quelques ammonites du Crétacé Algérien: Géol. Soc. France Mém., Paléont., f. 2–3, mém., no. 42, 86 p., 7 pls.

Powell, J. D., 1963, Cenomanian-Turonian (Cretaceous) ammonites from trans-Pecos Texas and northeastern Chihuahua, Mexico: Jour. Paleontology, v. 37, p. 309–322, 3 figs., Pl. 31–34

Powers, Sidney, 1926, Interior salt domes of Texas: Am. Assoc. Petroleum Geologists Bull., v. 10, p. 1–60, 1 pl.

Reeside, J. B., Jr., 1927, The *Scaphites*, an Upper Cretaceous ammonite group: U.S. Geol. Survey Prof. Paper 150-B, p. 21–40, 2 pls.

Reyment, R. A., 1955, The Cretaceous Ammonoidea of southern Nigeria and the southern Cameroons :Geol. Survey Nigeria Bull. 25, 112 p., 46 figs., 25 pls.

Roemer, Ferdinand, 1852, Die Kreidebildungen von Texas und ihre organischen Einschlüsse: Bonn, Adolph Marcus, 100 p., 10 pls.

Ruzhencev, V. E., 1960, Ammonoid classification problems: Jour. Paleontology, v. 34, p. 609–619, 4 figs.

Schlüter, Clemen, 1876, Cephalopoden der Oberen Kreide. 2, Palaeontographica: v. 24, 145 p., 55 pls.

Scott, Gayle, 1924, Some gerontic ammonites of the Duck Creek Formation: Texas Christian Univ. Quart., v. 1, 31 p., 9 pls.

—— 1926, Études stratigraphiques et paléontologiques sur les terrains crétacés du Texas: Univ. Grenoble Thèse, Faculty Sci., 218 p., 3 pls.

—— 1928, Ammonites of the genus *Dipoloceras* and a new *Hamites* from the Texas Cretaceous: Jour. Paleontology, v. 2, 108–118, 1 fig., Pls. 15, 16

Sharpe, Daniel, 1853–1857, Description of the fossil remains of Mollusca found in the Chalk of England. Pt. 1, Cephalopoda: Palaeont. Soc. London Mon., 68 p., 27 pls.

Shumard, B.F., 1854, Paleontology; description of the species of Carboniferous and Cretaceous fossils collected, p. 173–185 *in* Marcy, R. B., *Editor,* Exploration of the Red River of Louisiana in the year 1852: U.S. 33d Cong., 1st sess., House Executive Doc.

—— 1860, Descriptions of new Cretaceous fossils from Texas: Acad. Sci. St. Louis Trans., v. 1, no. 4, p. 590–610

Sowerby, J., 1812–1823, The mineral conchology of Great Britain: London, B. Meredith, 4 v., 383 pls.

Spath, L. F., 1923, On the ammonite horizons of the Gault and contiguous deposits: Geol. Survey Great Britain for 1922, Progress, Summary, Appendix 2, p. 139–149

—— 1923–1943, A monograph of the Ammonoidea of the Gault: Palaeont. Soc. London Mon., pt. 1, 1923; pts. 2, 3, 1925; pt. 4, 1926; pt. 5, 1927; p. 6, 1928; pt. 7, 1930; pt. 8, 1931; pt. 9, 1932; pt. 10, 1933 pt. 11, 1934; pt. 12, 1937; pt. 13, 1939; pt. 14, 1941; pt. 15, 1942; pt. 16, 1943: 787 p., 248 figs., 72 pls., 4 tables

—— 1926, On new ammonites from the English Chalk; Geol. Mag., v. 63, p. 77–83

Stephenson, L. W., 1941, The larger invertebrate fossils of the Navarro Group of Texas: Univ. Texas Bull. 4101, 641 p., 13 figs., 95 pls., 6 tables

—— 1952, Larger invertebrate fossils of the Woodbine Formation (Cenomanian) of Texas: U.S. Geol. Survey Prof. Paper 242, 226 p., 8 figs., 59 pls., 1 table

Stoliczka, F., 1866, Fossil Cephalopoda of the Cretaeous rocks of southern India: Geol. Survey India Mem., Palaeont. Indica, ser. 3, pts. 10–13, p. 155–216, 19 pls.

Swensen, A. J., 1963, Anisoceratidae and Hamitidae (Ammonoidea) from the Cretaceous of Texas and Utah: Brigham Young Univ. Geol. Studies, v. 9, pt. 2, p. 53–82, 21 figs., 5 pls.

White, C. A., 1877, The invertebrate fossils collected in portions of Nevada, Utah, Colorado, New Mexico and Arizona, by parties of the expeditions of 1871, 1872, 1873, and 1874: U.S. Geog. Surveys west of the one hundredth meridian, pt. 1, v. 4, p. 3–219, Pls. 1–19

—— 1880, Descriptions of new Cretaceous invertebrate fossils from Kansas and Texas: U.S. Natl. Mus. Proc. 2, p. 292–298

—— 1887, On new generic forms of Cretaceous Mollusca and their relation to other forms: Phila. Acad. Nat. Sci. Proc., p. 32–37

Whitney, F. L., 1911, Fauna of the Buda Limestone: Texas Acad. Sci. Proc. 12, 54 p., 12 pls.

Winton, W. M., 1925, The geology of Denton County: Univ. Texas Bull. 2544, 86 p., 8 figs., 21 pls., map

Winton, W. M., and Adkins, W. S., 1920, The geology of Tarrant County: Univ. Texas Bull. 1931, 122 p., 6 figs., 6 pls., 2 maps

Wright, C. W., 1953, Notes on Cretaceous ammonites. 1, Scaphitidae: Ann. Mag. Nat. History, v. 6, ser. 2, p. 473–476

Wright, C. W., and Wright, E. V., 1951, A survey of the fossil Cephalopoda of the Chalk of Great Britain: Palaeont. Soc. London Mon., 40 p.

Young, Keith, 1957, Upper Albian (Cretaceous) Ammonoidea from Texas: Jour. Paleontology, v. 31, p. 1–33, 3 figs., 10 pls.

—— 1958, Cenomanian (Cretaceous) ammonites from trans-Pecos Texas: Jour. Paleontology, v. 32, p. 286–294, 2 figs., Pls. 39, 40

—— 1963, Upper Cretaceous ammonites from the Gulf Coast of the United States: Univ. Texas Pub. 6304, 373 p., 34 figs., 82 pls., 13 tables

EXPLANATION OF PLATES 1–24

PLATE 1. HAMITIDAE AND ANISOCERATIDAE

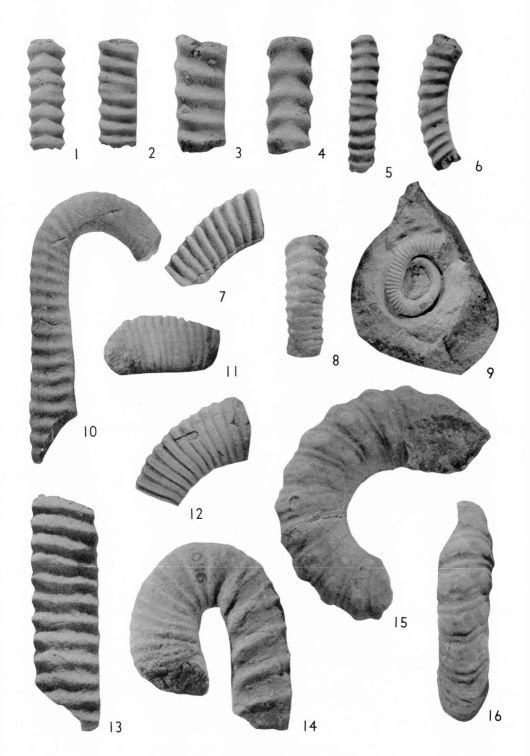

HAMITIDAE AND ANISOCERATIDAE

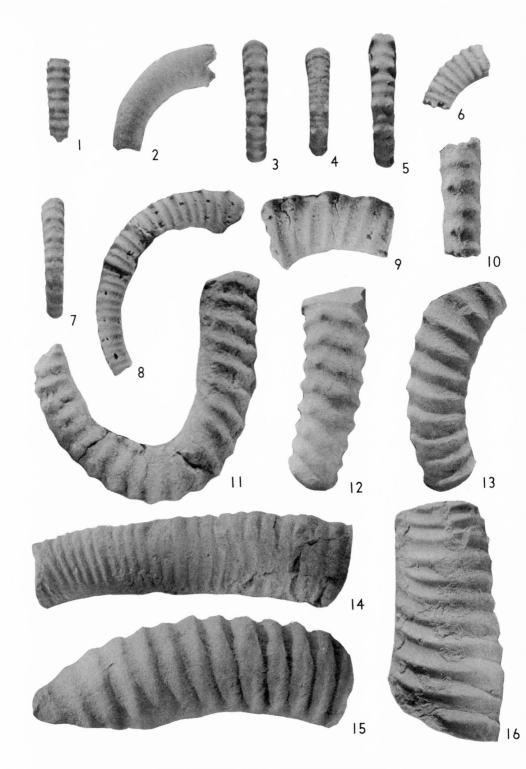

HAMITIDAE AND ANISOCERATIDAE

PLATE 2. HAMITIDAE AND ANISOCERATIDAE

PLATE 3.   BACULITIDAE

BACULITIDAE

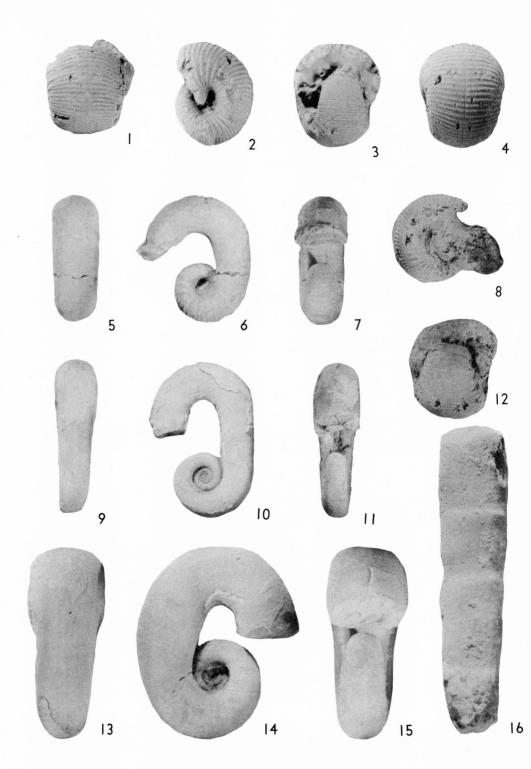

SCAPHITACEAE AND BACULITIDAE

PLATE 4. SCAPHITACEAE AND BACULITIDAE

PLATE 5. HAMITIDAE AND ANISOCERATIDAE

HAMITIDAE AND ANISOCERATIDAE

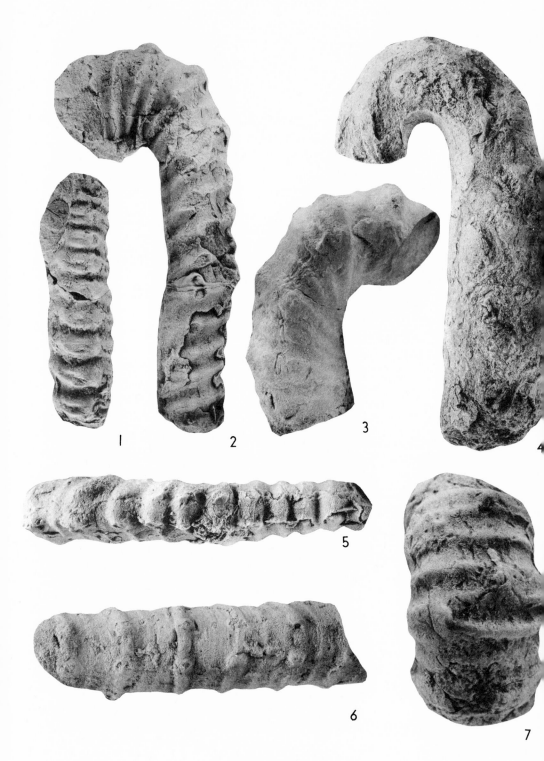

1   2   3   4

5

6

7

ANISOCERATIDAE

PLATE 6. ANISOCERATIDAE

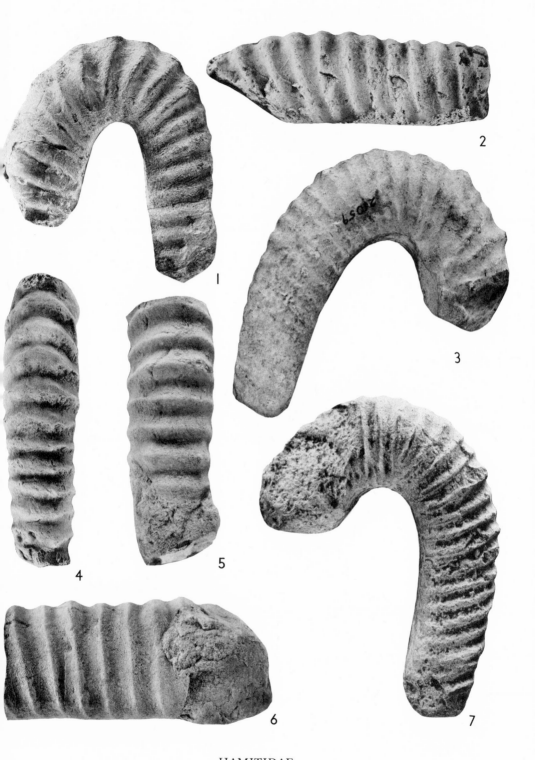

HAMITIDAE

TURRILITIDAE

PLATE 8. TURRILITIDAE

PLATE 9. TURRILITIDAE

TURRILITIDAE

1

2

3

4

5

TURRILITIDAE

PLATE 10. TURRILITIDAE

PLATE 11. TURRILITIDAE

1   2   3   4   5   6   7

TURRILITIDAE

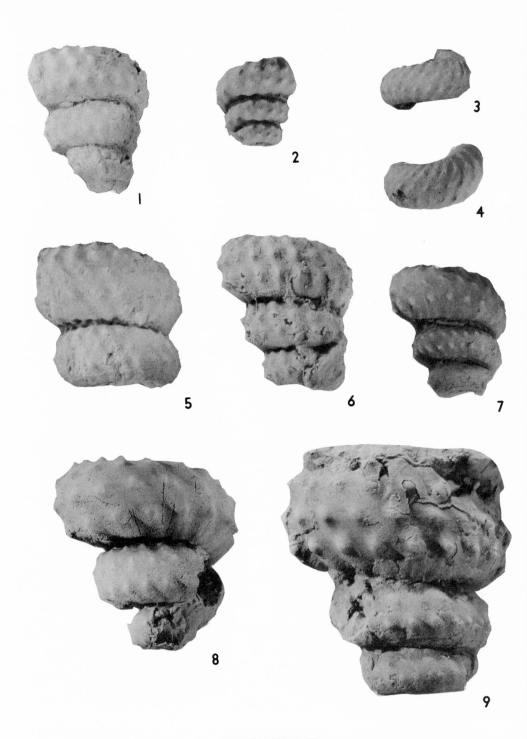

TURRILITIDAE

PLATE 12. TURRILITIDAE

PLATE 13. TURRILITIDAE

TURRILITIDAE

TURRILITIDAE

PLATE 14. TURRILITIDAE

PLATE 15. TURRILITIDAE

1

2

3

4

5

TURRILITIDAE

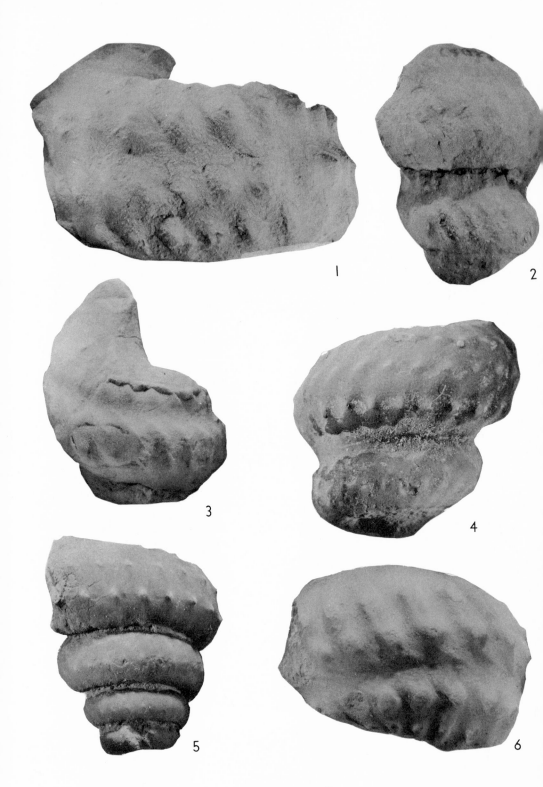

1

2

3

4

5

6

TURRILITIDAE

PLATE 16. TURRILITIDAE

Plate 17. TURRILITIDAE

Figures   Page

1–16. *Mariella (Plesioturrilites) bosquensis* (Adkins).   47
    1, paedomorphic variety, compare ornamentation on same-size whorl of 2, BEG
    35337; 2,6, average specimen in all characteristics, note portion of body chamber,
    BEG 35347; 3, dextral, BEG 35339; 4, dextral, oblique ribbing, BEG 35340; 5,
    paedomorphic variety, BEG 35344; 7, holotype, note fewer tubercles than on
    average of population 2, BEG 20990; 8, paedomorphic variety, BEG 35345; 9,
    BEG 35341; 10, 14, apertural margin and body chamber, two views, BEG 35342;
    11, BEG 35343; 12, greater number of tubercles than average of population,
    BEG 35348; 13, same as 12, BEG 35349; 15, BEG 35336; 16, accelerated individual,
    BEG 35335. All from Del Rio (× 2.5)

TURRILITIDAE

TURRILITIDAE

PLATE 18. TURRILITIDAE

PLATE 19. TURRILITIDAE

TURRILITIDAE

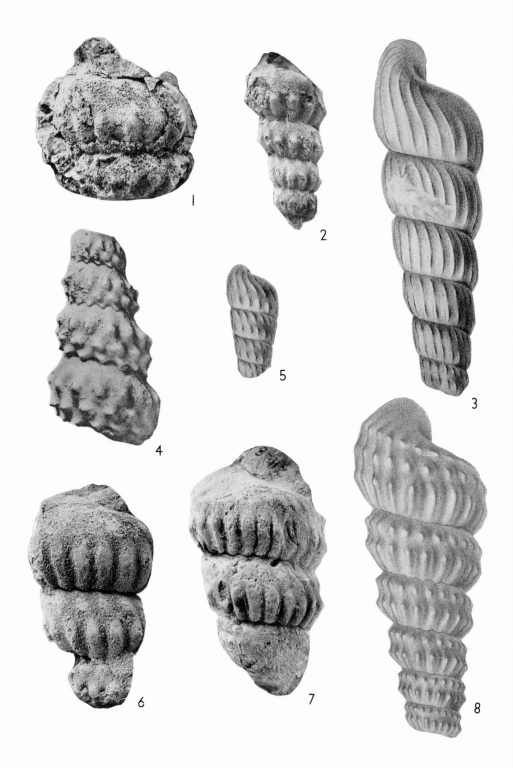

TURRILITIDAE

PLATE 20. TURRILITIDAE

PLATE 21. SCAPHITINAE

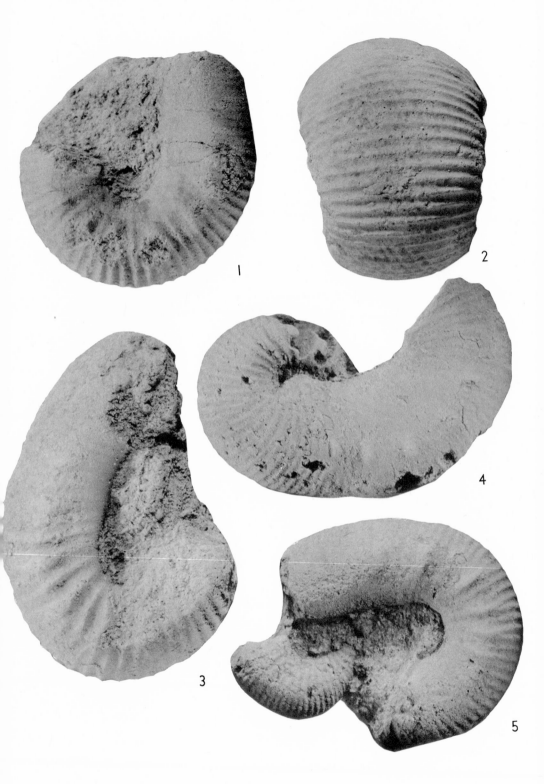

SCAPHITINAE

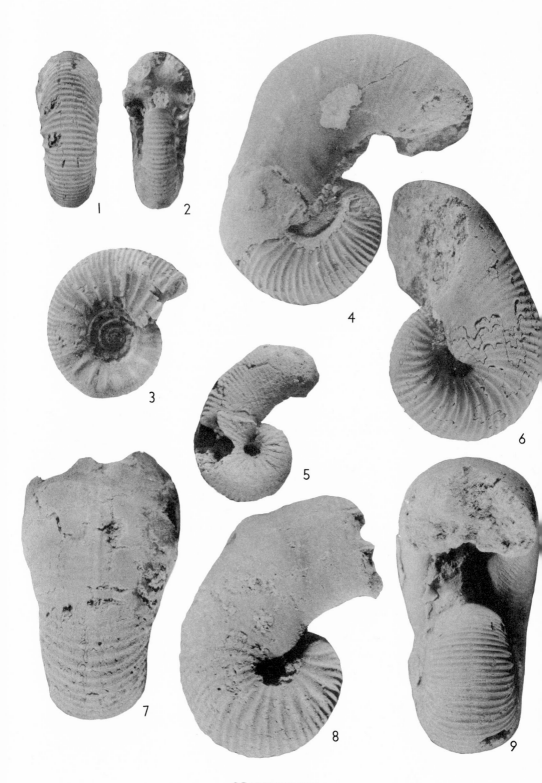

SCAPHITINAE

PLATE 22. SCAPHITINAE

Plate 23.   OTOSCAPHITINAE

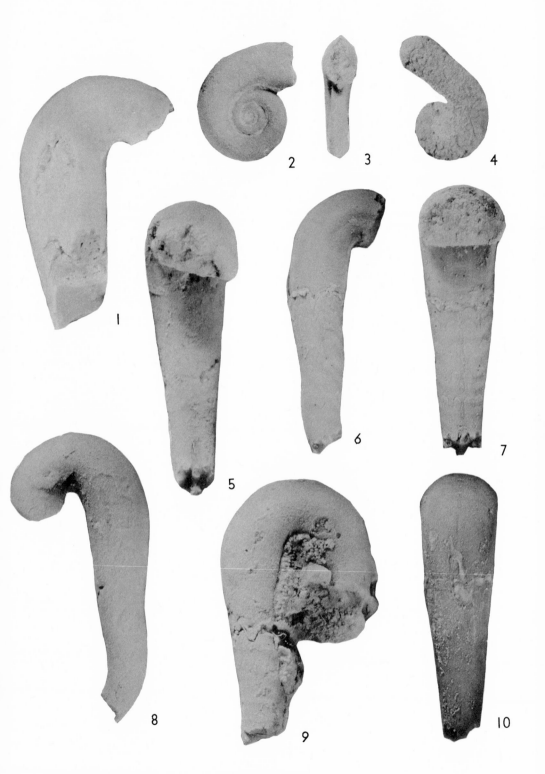

OTOSCAPHITINAE

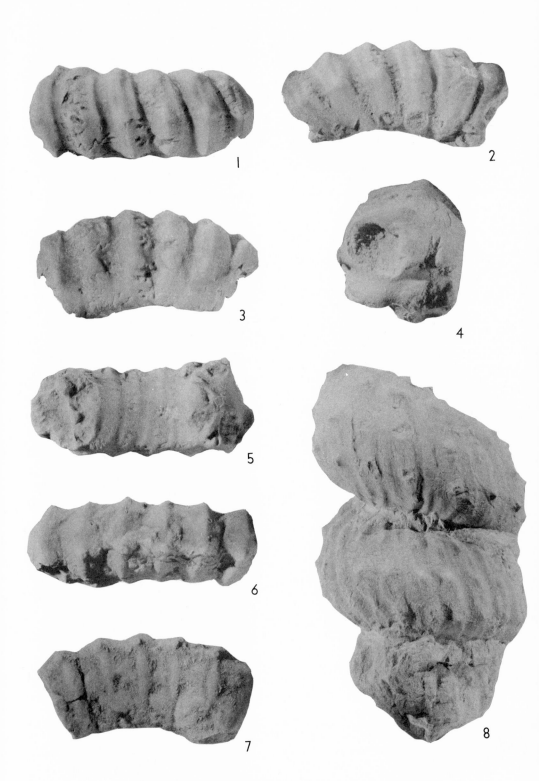

PHLYCTICRIOCERATIDAE AND TURRILITIDAE

PLATE 24. PHLYCTICRIOCERATIDAE AND TURRILITIDAE

INDEX[3]

acceleration, 6
— in *Mariella (Mariella) worthensis*, 17
Adkins, W.S., 3, 5, 7, 11, 23, 24, 25, 35, 41, 42, 45, 47, 48, 49, 50, 55, 56, 57, 58, 60, 61
Adkins and Winton, 3, 34, 45, 46, 57, 58
aequatorialis subzone, 11, 13
aequatorialis-dispar subzones, 13
aequatorialis-substuderi subzones, 13, 14
Africa, occurrence of *Carthaginites*, 56
Alaska, occurrence of *Otoscaphites*, 63
Albian, Middle, 13
— Middle in Europe, 36
— occurrence of *Hypoturrilites*, 52
Algeria, occurrence of *Scaphites*, 22
Allocrioceras, 31
    annulatum, 11, **31**, 32, 70, 74
        suture, 31
        whorl section, 30
    dentonense, 11, 31, **32**, 70, 74
        whorl section, 32
    n. sp. aff. *ellipticum*, 31
    hazzardi, 31
    larvatum, 11, 31, **32**
    pariense, 11, **31**, 32, 71
        whorl section, 32
    ? *rotundatum*, 11, **33**
    sp., 16, 70
        Mexico, 31
    woodsi, 31
ancestor, *Pseudhelicoceras*, 37
ancestral stock, Turrilitidae, 35
Ancyloceras annulatum, 31
    annulatus, 31
    bendirei, 26
Anderson, F. M., 4
Anisoceras, 24
    armatum, 7, 9, 13, 14, **25**, 27, 74, 75
        cfr., 25
        whorl section, 25
    bendirei, 9, **26**, 74
        whorl section, 25
    perarmatum, 9, 13, 14, **25**, 26, 75
    sp. aff. *A. plicatile*, 8, **27**, 70
        whorl section, 25
    salei, 7, 13, **26**, 75
    sp., 11
    saussureanum, 13, 25, 26, 27
    subarcuatum, 8, 13, **27**, 75
        whorl section, 28
Anisoceratidae, 6
    evolution, 24
Aquilla, Texas, 50
Arcadia Park Formation, 10
Arkell and others, 5, 14, 16, 19, 20, 22, 24, 28, 33, 34, 35, 38, 40, 45, 50, 53, 56, 57, 60

Arlington Heights, Texas, 27
Astier, M. J., 3
auritus subzone, 11, 13
Aurora Limestone, 10
    occurrence of *Plesioturrilites*, 46
Austin Formation, 5
    baculitids, 22

Baculites anceps, 22
    annulatus, 22
    aspero-anceps, 22
    baculoides, 24
    claviformis, 22
    columna, 22
    comanchensis, 23, 24
    cfr. *gaudini*, 23
    gracilus, 22
    sp. aff. *B. gracilus*, 22
    ovatus, 22
    sp. Winton and Adkins, 23
    taylorensis, 22
    undatus, 22
Baculitidae, 6
baculitids, 4, 5
    classification, 22
Belton, Texas, 27, 54
biostratigraphy, baculitids, 22
Bonn, Germany, 46
    Museum, 54
Boquillas Flags, 14
— Formation, 10
    occurrence of *Hypoturrilites*, 53
    — *Ostlingoceras*, 36, 37
    west Texas, 31
Böse, Emil, 3, 5, 11, 14, 20, 21, 23, 24, 25, 42, 43, 44, 48, 59, 60
Breistroffer, Maurice, 4, 11, 12, 36, 39, 40, 45, 57
Breslau, Poland, 42
Britton Formation, 10, 16, 32
    occurrence of *Allocrioceras annulatum*, 31
    — *Allocrioceras larvatum*, 33
    — *Otoscaphites*, 63
    — *Worthoceras*, 62
Buda Limestone, 6
    occurrence of *Carthaginites*, 56
    — *Mariella wysogorskii*, 43
Bureau of Economic Geology, Austin, Texas, 5, 7

caenogenesis, 17, 48, 49, 50
California
    occurrence of *Plesioturrilites*, 45
    — *Pseudhelicoceras*, 38
Camacho, Mexico, 24, 43

[3] Numbers in **boldface** indicate detailed descriptions.